McGRAW-HILL READING

Phonics and Phonemic Awareness

Grade 3   Practice Book

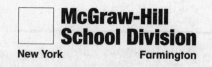

McGraw-Hill
School Division

New York   Farmington

Contents

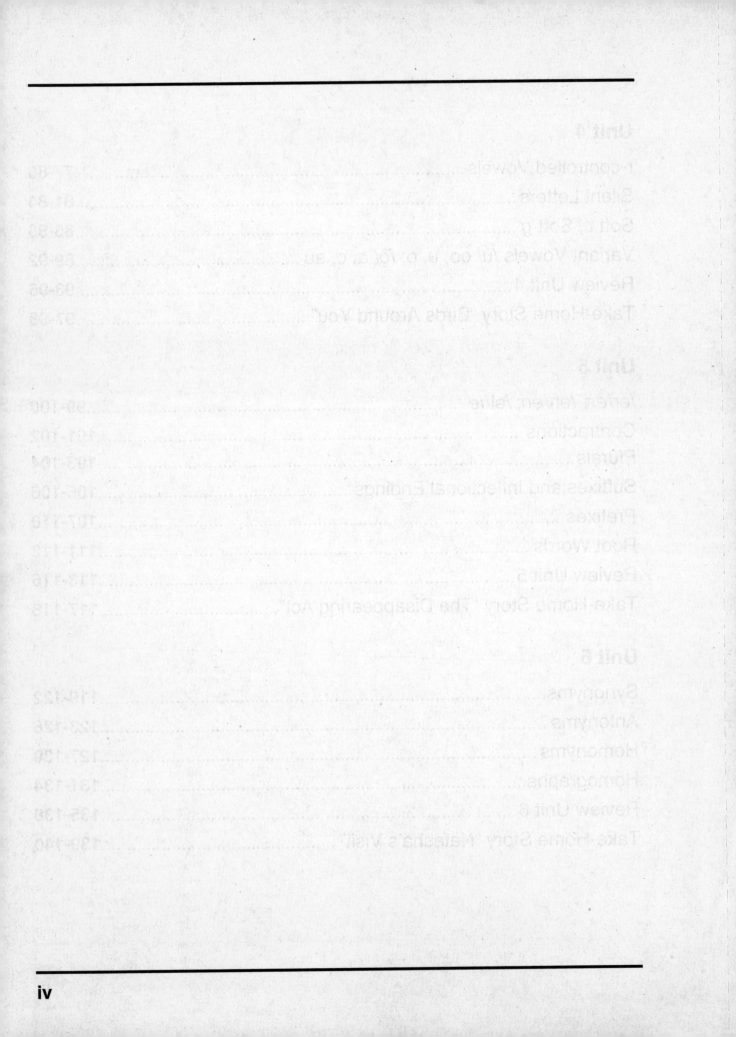

Listen for Initial Consonants

Draw a circle around the pictures whose names do not have the same beginning sound as the first picture in each row.

Listen for Final Consonants

Draw a line under the pictures whose names do not have the same ending sound as the first picture in each row.

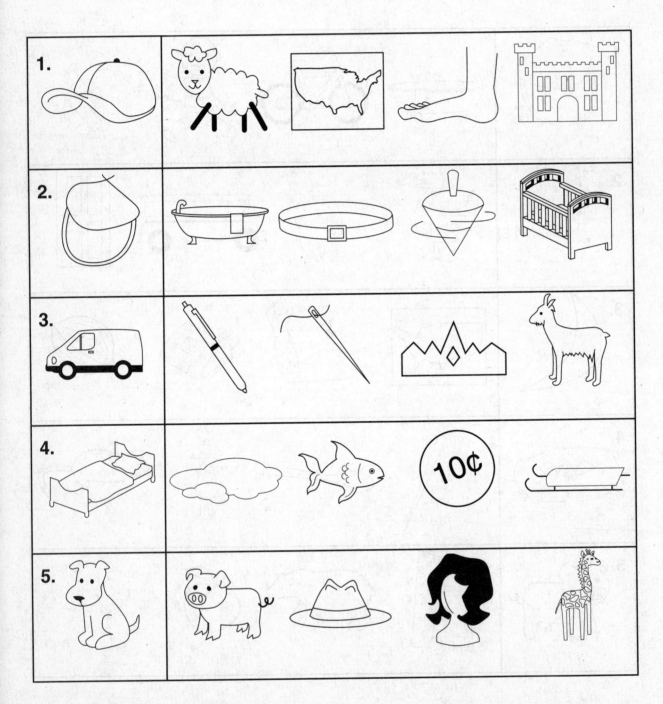

Initial Consonants

Name each picture. Write the letter that stands for the sound at the beginning of the word.

1. _____

2. _____

3. _____

4. _____

5. _____

6. _____

7. _____

8. _____

9. _____

10. _____

11. _____

12. _____

Final Consonants

Name each picture. Write the letter that stands for the sound at the end of the word.

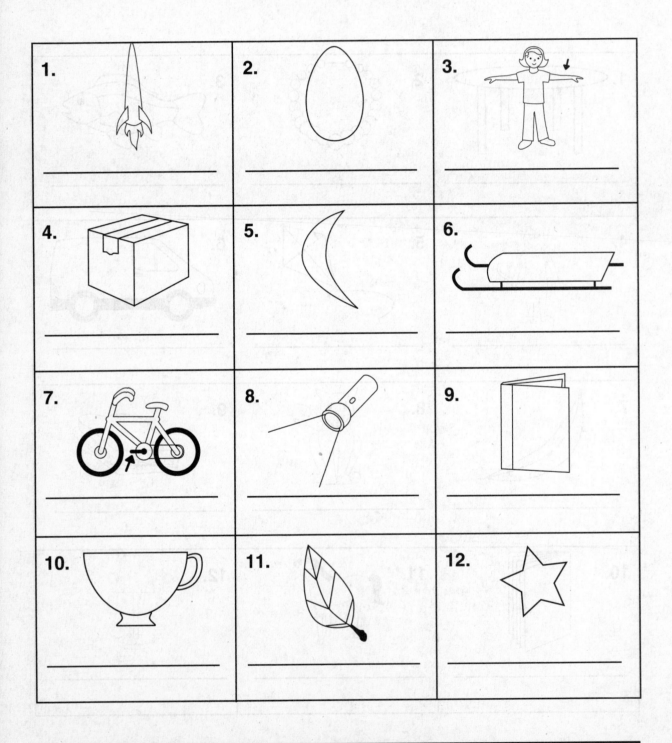

1. _____

2. _____

3. _____

4. _____

5. _____

6. _____

7. _____

8. _____

9. _____

10. _____

11. _____

12. _____

Initial and Final Consonants

Name each picture. Draw a circle around the letter that completes the word and write it on the line.

1. f h d

_____og

2. p b m

_____en

3. h s f

_____ad

4. m n l

_____amp

5. m n t

_____est

6. t r p

rocke_____

7. m v n

_____an

8. t b s

bu_____

9. j g c

_____irl

10. p d r

shi_____

11. j g d

plu_____

12. c b d

_____esk

Initial and Final Consonants

Name each picture. Draw a circle around the letter that completes the word and write it on the line.

1. d m n

clow_____

2. p b m

_____ag

3. f b r

dee_____

4. m n t

he_____

5. d l n

clou_____

6. g l b

_____oose

7. l d k

hoo_____

8. n m w

cla_____

9. j g d

_____ime

10. s x f

fo_____

11. p r l

snai_____

12. v b z

_____est

Listen for Short Vowels

Draw a circle around the pictures whose names do not have the same vowel sound as the first picture in each row.

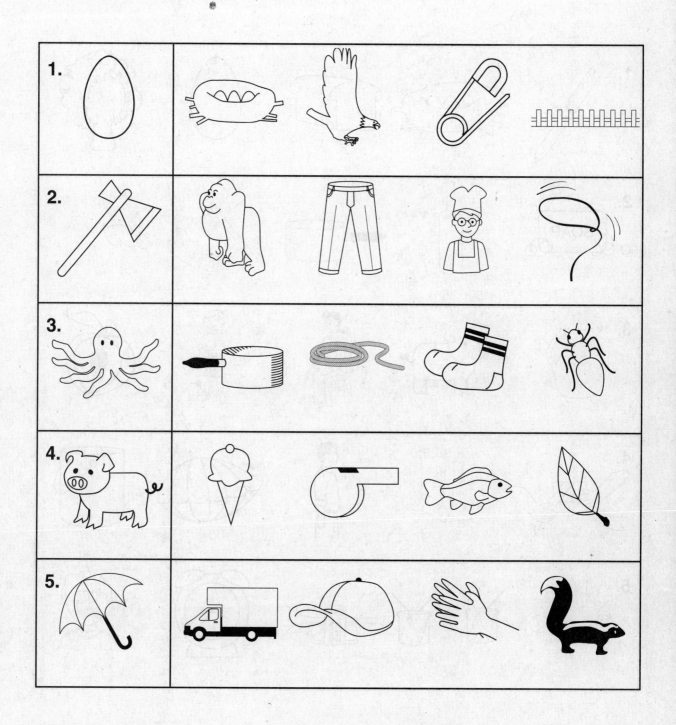

Listen for Short Vowels

Name the pictures in each row. Put an **X** on the picture that does not have the same vowel sound as the others.

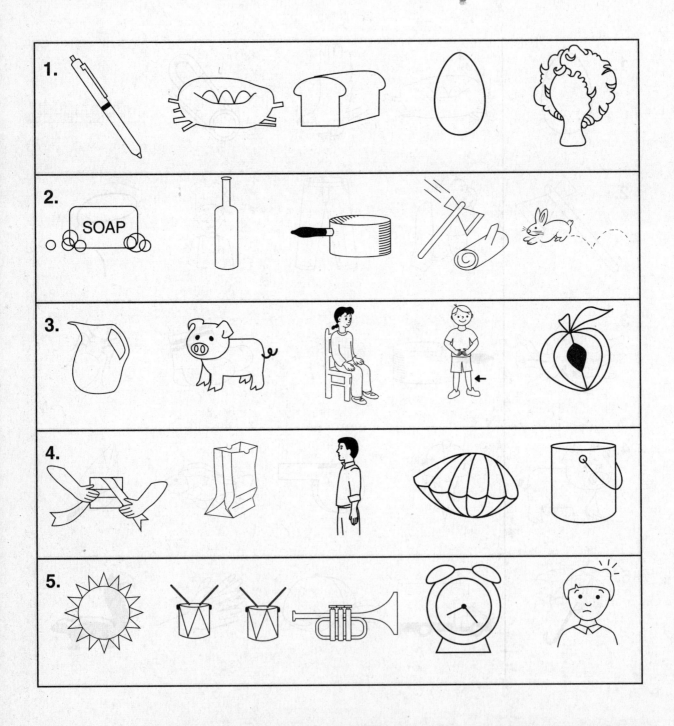

Short Vowels

Draw a circle around each word that has the same vowel sound as the name of the picture.

1. bread / edge / steady / green	**2.** fasten / paint / chap / last	**3.** listen / limp / white / whistle
4. chop / block / blow / foxes	**5.** head / fender / left / street	**6.** supper / true / trust / fumble
7. brave / flap / camel / strap	**8.** moon / popcorn / stop / mopped	**9.** thin / ninety / itch / jiggle
10. slush / tub / crumb / flute	**11.** pane / planet / hatch / brad	**12.** head / rest / heed / stress

Short Vowels

The letter at the beginning of each sentence stands for a short vowel. Read the sentence. Then draw a circle around each word that has that short vowel sound.

a   **1.** I go to art class after school on Fridays.

e   **2.** My best pal, Ted, goes with me.

o   **3.** I got a new box of paints for my class.

i   **4.** The class is different than last year.

u   **5.** After lunch on Friday, the time just drags.

e   **6.** I got a letter from my cousin Betty.

i   **7.** She wants to visit me in the fall.

o   **8.** I hope she will attend our band's concert in October.

u   **9.** Tim plays trumpet and I play drums.

a   **10.** My sister plays in the jazz band.

Short Vowels

Draw a circle around the letter that will finish the word in each sentence. Write the letter on the line.

1. My favorite season is w_____nter.   a e i o u

2. We skate on the p_____nd near my school.   a e i o u

3. Last week the ice was eight inches th_____ck. a e i o u

4. The surface m_____lted a little yesterday.   a e i o u

5. B_____t it froze again quickly.   a e i o u

6. On Sunday, Dad treated us all to br_____nch. a e i o u

7. It was really a birthday g_____ft to my mom.   a e i o u

8. I had Fr_____nch toast and melon.   a e i o u

9. Mom had _____pple pancakes.   a e i o u

10. Everything was h_____t and delicious.   a e i o u

Short Vowels

Draw a line to the word that answers each riddle. Then draw a circle around the letters that stand for a short vowel sound.

1. This is something used to set a broken bone.

2. A train runs on these.

3. This is the opposite of *light*.

4. You can store things on this for your computer.

5. You have these in your jacket.

6. You might do this if you are embarrassed.

7. This is a member of the ape family.

8. Gold or silver could be called this.

9. This can be an opening in a ship, floor, or roof.

10. You can train a dog to do this.

heavy

pockets

disk

splint

treasure

chimp

hatch

fetch

blush

tracks

Grade 3 / **20**

Listen for Consonant Blends

In each row, put an **X** on the pictures whose names do not begin with the same sounds as the first picture.

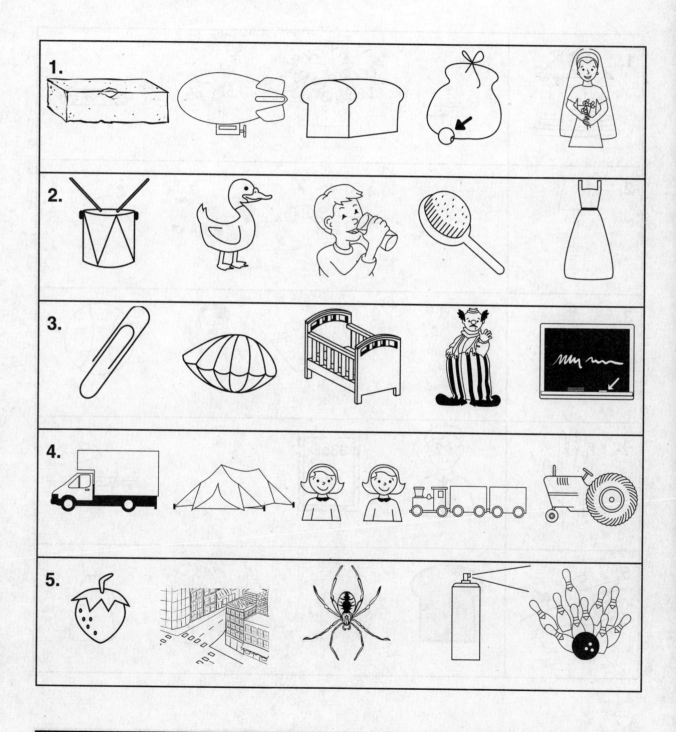

Listen for Consonant Blends

Draw a circle around the pictures whose names end with the same sounds as the first picture in each row.

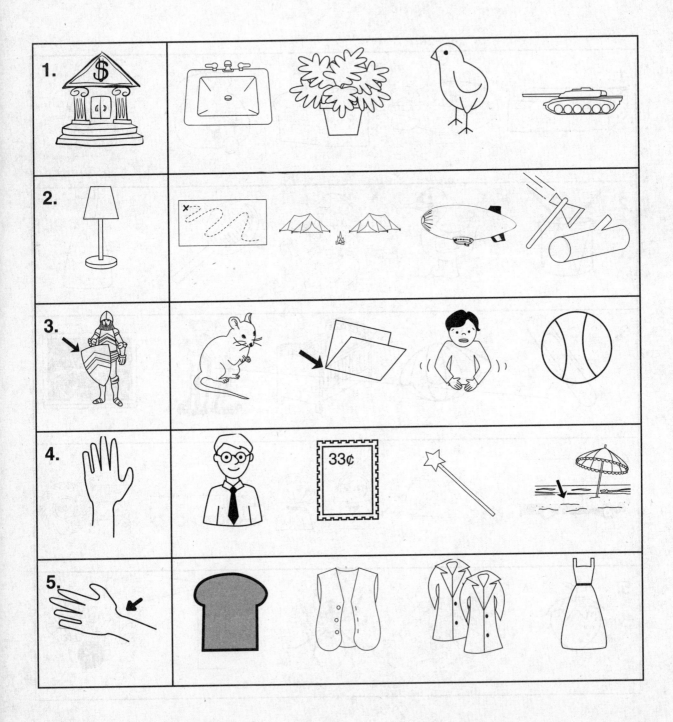

Consonant Blends

Name each picture. Find the missing consonant blend in the box.
Write the letters on the line.

sp	st	sw	sk	sm	sn
sl	mp	ng	nt	str	

1. _____ing

2. _____unk

3. wi_____

4. pai_____

5. _____oon

6. cha_____

7. _____oke

8. _____ates

9. _____ap

10. _____eaker

11. ne_____

12. _____ipper

Consonant Blends

Name each picture. If it **begins** with a blend, find the blend in the first box and draw a circle around it. If the picture name **ends** with a blend, find the blend in the second box and draw a circle around it.

1.	2.	3.
sl sw ld st	sk scr st mt	sp st nt nk
4.	5.	6.
dr dl nt mp	br bl nk mp	sm sn lk lt
7.	8.	9.
gl gr lm ld	mr ml ld lk	st str st nt
10.	11.	12.
tw tr st nt	fl fr lg ng	dr pr mp mt

Grade 3   12

Consonant Blends

Read each sentence. Add the missing consonant blend to the word.

str	fr	sl	sk	st	sm	nt	nd	mp

1. My _____iend Bridget and I _____ept out in her yard last night.

2. We went out at du_____ to look for shooting _____ars.

3. We put up a te_____ and rolled our sleeping bags out on the grou_____.

4. We _____etched out on our backs to watch the _____y.

5. The ground was da_____ and the grass _____elled sweet.

6. There wasn't any wi_____, but there was a little mi_____ in the air.

7. I was the fir_____ to see a star _____eak across the sky.

8. Soon there were just too many to cou_____.

Consonant Blends

Draw a line to the word that answers each riddle. Then draw a circle around the consonant blend in each word.

1. They might carry you on this if you are hurt.

2. This is a plant with a three-part leaf.

3. When you beep a car horn you do this.

4. This is a kind of sea creature.

5. This is another word for "planet."

6. This word means "kind of dog," like collies or hounds.

7. This is a beautiful, white water bird.

8. This is a dark red color.

9. This is a kind of material.

10. This means a piece.

11. This means to let someone use for a while.

12. You might put names on this.

13. A cat can do this.

14. If you step on a blueberry, you do this to it.

15. This is the bone that protects your brain.

honk

clam

world

stretcher

swan

clover

crimson

felt

slice

breed

skull

squash

list

lend

scratch

McGraw-Hill School Division

Listen for Digraphs

Draw a circle around the pictures whose names have the same beginning sound as the first picture in each row.

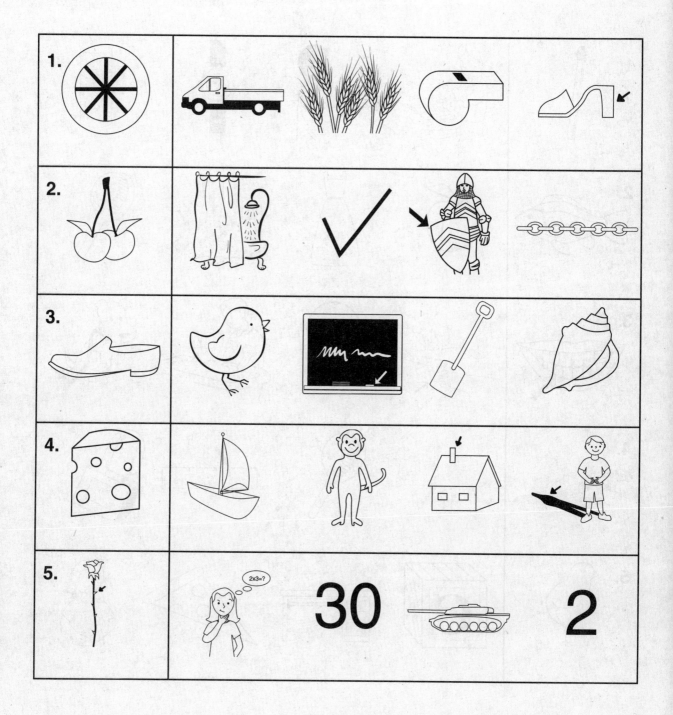

Name_____ Date_____

Listen for Digraphs

Put an **X** on the pictures whose names do not have the same ending sound as the first picture in each line.

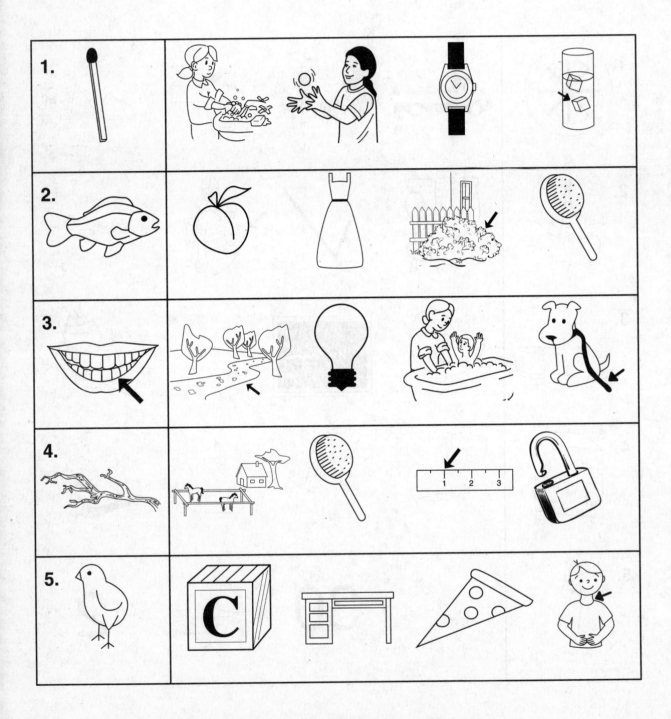

1.

2.

3.

4.

5.

Digraphs

Read the sentences. Draw a circle around the words that have the digraphs **ch, tch, sh, wh,** or **ph.** Then write the word on the line.

1. My Uncle Bob likes to whittle. _____

2. He carved this dolphin for me. _____

3. He started with a small chunk of wood. _____

4. The wood he picked was white pine. _____

5. He used a very sharp knife. _____

6. I watched as he worked. _____

7. At first, he carved off big chips. _____

8. I began to see the shape he was making. _____

9. Finally, the carving was finished. _____

10. "It's wonderful," I whispered. _____

Digraphs

Draw a line to the word that answers each riddle. Then draw a circle around the consonant digraph in each word.

1. Smoke comes out of this.

2. This noise comes with lightning.

3. Roses have these; so do raspberries.

4. This number comes after twelve.

5. You have two of these on a bicycle.

6. This means to talk.

7. This is the opposite of north.

8. This is a kind of bird.

9. Fruit trees grow here.

10. You can see the ocean here.

thorns
chimney
wheels
south
thunder
thirteen
pheasant
orchard
seashore
chat

Digraphs

Write the word from the box that completes each sentence.

dolphins	both	bunch	which	fish
lunch	watch	truth	mouth	whale

1. I like to _____ television shows about animals.

2. Last week I saw one about the great blue _____.

3. Did you know that whales are related to _____?

4. I think _____ animals are interesting.

5. Some people think whales are _____, but they are mammals.

6. _____ is your favorite fruit?

7. Tell the _____, do you prefer an apple or a peach?

8. Just thinking about a juicy peach can make my _____ water.

9. It is fun to eat a _____ of grapes.

10. Gosh, I wish it was time for _____!

Digraphs

Draw a circle around the letters that will finish the word in each sentence.
Write the letters on the line.

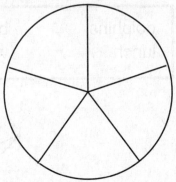

1. Phil did a report on the televison shows
   _____ird graders watch.
   wh   ch   th

2. He made a pie gra_____ to show what he
   learned.   ch   ph   tch

3. He learned to make a graph like that in ma_____ class.
   th   ph   sh

4. Graphs are a good way to _____ow information.
   ch   sh   tch

5. You'll be astoni_____ed when you see what this one shows.
   ph   sh   tch

6. Rick _____ooses books about animals.
   ch   sh   tch

7. Phoebe enjoys a good biogra_____y.
   th   ph   sh

8. I like stories with a strong message, or
   _____eme.   th   ph   sh

9. My bro_____er likes sports stories.
   ch   th   sh

10. He read one about a famous baseball pi_____er.
    ch   sh   tch

McGraw-Hill School Division

Name_____ Date_____

Review Initial/Final Consonants; Short Vowels; Consonant Blends/Digraphs

Find the name of each picture in the box. Write it on the line.

trapeze	latch	shelf	chipmunk	measure	elephant
shears	bread	spray	wheelbarrow	trophy	scratch

1. _____

2. _____

3. _____

4. _____

5. _____

6. _____

7. _____

8. _____

9. _____

10. _____

11. _____

12. _____

Review Initial/Final Consonants; Short Vowels; Consonant Blends/Digraphs

Draw a circle around the letter or letters that will finish the word in each sentence. Write the letters on the line.

1. Mrs. Mitchell is a pl———sant neighbor.
    ea   e   o

2. She has red hair and fre———les.
    ch   ck   tch

3. She often gives us fre——— baked bread.
    ch   sh   tch

4. Sometimes she gives us cookies, inst———d.
    ea   a   i

5. But her cherry pie is the be———!   sh   st   ld

6. My little bro———er is learning to read and write.
    sh   wh   th

7. He can write the letters of the al———abet.   sh   ph   th

8. He knows most of their sou———s.   nt   nd   ld

9. Does he know that *sh* and *ch* are digra———s?
    ph   th   sh

10. No, but he knows that *dr* and *tr* are ———ends.   fr   pl   bl

Name_____ Date_____

Review Initial/Final Consonants; Short Vowels; Consonant Blends/Digraphs

Draw a line to the word that answers each riddle.

1. This word means "not real."

2. A candle has this.

3. This is what a spider can do.

4. Use this to light a fire.

5. A thorny bush could do this.

6. A hen is one.

7. Poison ivy can give you this.

8. What you do before you work out.

9. This is the first meal of the day.

10. This is a tiny bit of something.

wick

match

chicken

phony

spin

breakfast

speck

scratch

rash

stretch

Review Initial/Final Consonants; Short Vowels; Consonant Blends/Digraphs

Draw a circle around the word that completes the sentence and write it on the line.

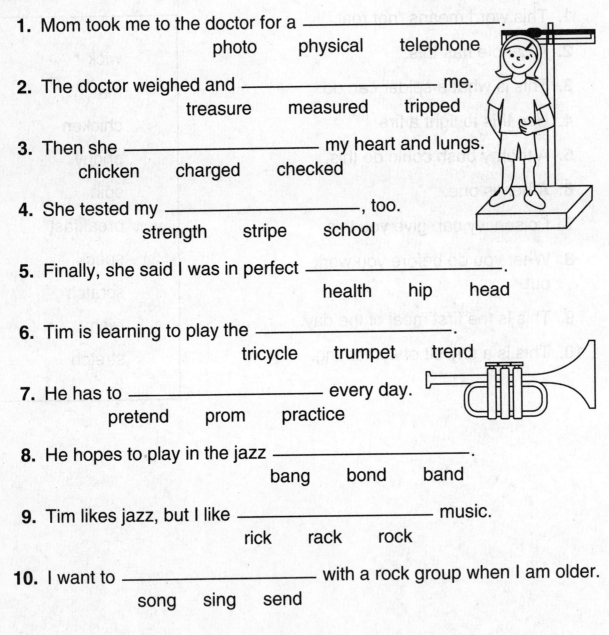

1. Mom took me to the doctor for a _____.

                photo   physical   telephone

2. The doctor weighed and _____ me.

                treasure   measured   tripped

3. Then she _____ my heart and lungs.

                chicken   charged   checked

4. She tested my _____, too.

                strength   stripe   school

5. Finally, she said I was in perfect _____.

                health   hip   head

6. Tim is learning to play the _____.

                tricycle   trumpet   trend

7. He has to _____ every day.

                pretend   prom   practice

8. He hopes to play in the jazz _____.

                bang   bond   band

9. Tim likes jazz, but I like _____ music.

                rick   rack   rock

10. I want to _____ with a rock group when I am older.

                song   sing   send

I wish I could say we won the game. We didn't.

The Bisons scored another run the next inning.

But Coach said to us, "You Mammoths can be really proud of how you played that game. You never gave up! You're all champs in my book!"

And we felt like it—me most of all.

One of them was me. I hadn't had a hit in six games.

Somehow, Slim, our pitcher, managed to hold the Bisons to just one hit. They didn't score any more runs, and the inning was over. It was still 6 to 5 and it was our turn to bat again.

After two wild pitches, Joe hit an easy ground ball to the first baseman. He stepped on the bag. One out.

The team groaned. "It's no use," someone said. "We won't even tie."

Fold the right side back on the long center line. Then fold the top half under the bottom half on the short center line. Cut open the tops of the pages.

The Champs

It was the next to last inning of the last game of the season. If the Mammoths could just win this game against the Bisons, we'd make it to the playoffs.

But the score was six to four, and the Bisons had beaten us every game this season. Our best hitter was out with a sprained ankle, too.

It wasn't hopeless, though. We had two players on base. Jan had hit a single past the second baseman and Chet had walked. Now Rich was up next.

But the next batter struck out. After that, Peg hit into a double play and the inning was over.

"All right now, Mammoths, it's not over," said the coach. "If we can keep them from scoring, we have another chance next inning."

"Sure," I heard Rich grumble. "The worst hitters are up next inning."

Then I stepped forward and let my bat just nudge the ball. It landed fair and rolled to a stop a few feet in front of home plate. The pitcher and catcher both charged the ball and crashed into each other as Ned scored the tying run!

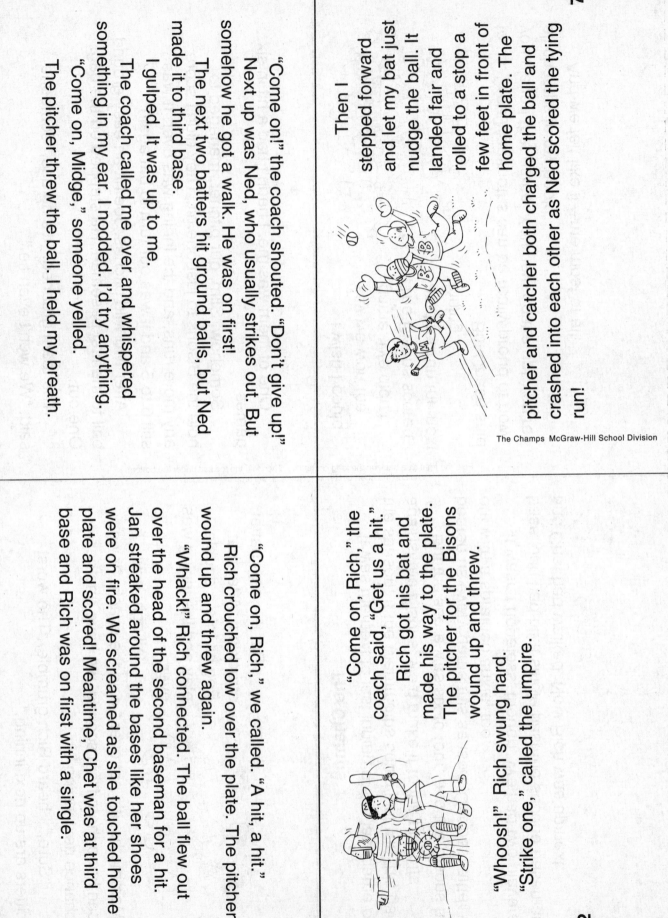

The Champs McGraw-Hill School Division

"Come on!" the coach shouted. "Don't give up!"

Next up was Ned, who usually strikes out. But somehow he got a walk. He was on first!

The next two batters hit ground balls, but Ned made it to third base.

The coach called me over and whispered something in my ear. I nodded. I'd try anything.

"Come on, Midge," someone yelled.

The pitcher threw the ball. I held my breath.

"Come on, Rich," we called. "A hit, a hit."

Rich crouched low over the plate. The pitcher wound up and threw again.

"Whack!" Rich connected. The ball flew out over the head of the second baseman for a hit. Jan streaked around the bases like her shoes were on fire. We screamed as she touched home plate and scored! Meantime, Chet was at third base and Rich was on first with a single.

"Come on, Rich," the coach said, "Get us a hit."

Rich got his bat and made his way to the plate. The pitcher for the Bisons wound up and threw.

"Whoosh!" Rich swung hard.

"Strike one," called the umpire.

Listen for Long *a*

Name the pictures in each row. Put an **X** on the picture that does not have the long **a** sound.

Long *a*

Draw a circle around each word that has the same long **a** sound as the name of the picture.

1. plain pear pansy lake	**2.** drain clam stray pliers	**3.** vases wait drives strap
4. receive neighbor take what	**5.** stay chain dribble dandy	**6.** praise proud beads stake
7. test brave tail wash	**8.** trick shake sway tinsel	**9.** pester sprain pump play
10. 8 freight little gain plan	**11.** weigh watch contain ride	**12.** water shame await pass

McGraw-Hill School Division

Long *a*

Draw a circle around the word that has the long **a** sound as in *clay*.
Write the letters that stand for the sound.

1. We have new neighbors on the block. _____

2. There is one girl named Sara. _____

3. Another girl is called Gail. _____

4. The three of us like to play together. _____

5. It rained hard last week. _____

6. We stayed indoors a lot. _____

7. We painted pretty pictures to hang up. _____

8. We made a yummy treat in the kitchen. _____

9. Mom said we should get paid for our cooking. _____

10. We felt good when Mom praised us. _____

Long *a*

Draw a circle around the word that has the same long **a** sound as in *pail*.
Then write the word on the line.

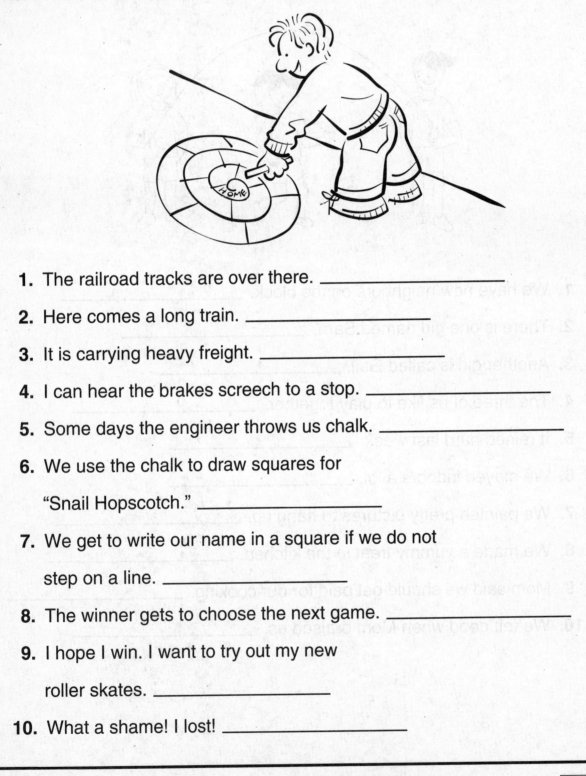

1. The railroad tracks are over there. _____

2. Here comes a long train. _____

3. It is carrying heavy freight. _____

4. I can hear the brakes screech to a stop. _____

5. Some days the engineer throws us chalk. _____

6. We use the chalk to draw squares for

   "Snail Hopscotch." _____

7. We get to write our name in a square if we do not

   step on a line. _____

8. The winner gets to choose the next game. _____

9. I hope I win. I want to try out my new

   roller skates. _____

10. What a shame! I lost! _____

Listen for Long *e*

Draw a circle around each picture that has the long **e** sound as in *feet*.

Long *e*

Find the word in the box that will finish each sentence. Write it on the line.

beeper	believe	cleaned	deeds	green
leaking	Peterson	seemed	thirty	weak

1. Dad always told me to try to do good _____.

2. Yesterday, I saw that the pipe under our sink was _____.

3. I called Mr. _____, our plumber.

4. He said that some of our pipes were old and _____.

5. He used his _____ to call for some help.

6. We had to wait about _____ minutes.

7. You won't _____ this, but the water turned colors!

8. First it was as _____ as grass, then red as a beet.

9. It _____ as if someone was using paints.

10. Dad just thinks that all our pipes have to be _____ more often.

McGraw-Hill School Division

Long *e*

Draw a circle around the word that has the long **e** sound. Then write it on the line.

1. I was not happy with the news._____

2. Mom said I had to go get my teeth checked today.

   _____

3. My dentist is a neat person, and I'm not afraid

   of her. _____

4. But today I have a ticket for the Monkey rock

   concert. _____

5. I have a seat in the front row. _____

6. Mom said I might be able to go to the dentist next week.

   _____

7. Mom said Pete, my neighbor, may go instead.

   _____

8. That would be such a relief! _____

9. I owe him a big treat for taking my place. _____

10. I think I will give him my best key ring. _____

Long *e*

Draw a line to the word that answers each riddle. Then draw a circle around the letters that stand for the long **e** sound.

1. It is like a brook.	chimney
2. It is thirty times two.	leech
3. It carries smoke from a fire.	freezing
4. This worm lives in water and feeds off other animals.	sixty
5. It is this when water turns to ice.	stream
6. All Americans enjoy this.	fleas
7. If you cut yourself, you will ————.	teacher
8. Dogs don't like these insects.	freedom
9. This is the person who grades your papers.	fleet
10. This is a group of ships.	bleed

Listen for Long *i*

Draw a circle around each picture that has the long **i** sound as in *hive*.

Long *i*

Find the name of each picture in the box. Write it on the line.

chimes	hive	iron	light	tie	pipe
smile	wire	dime	spider	stripes	night

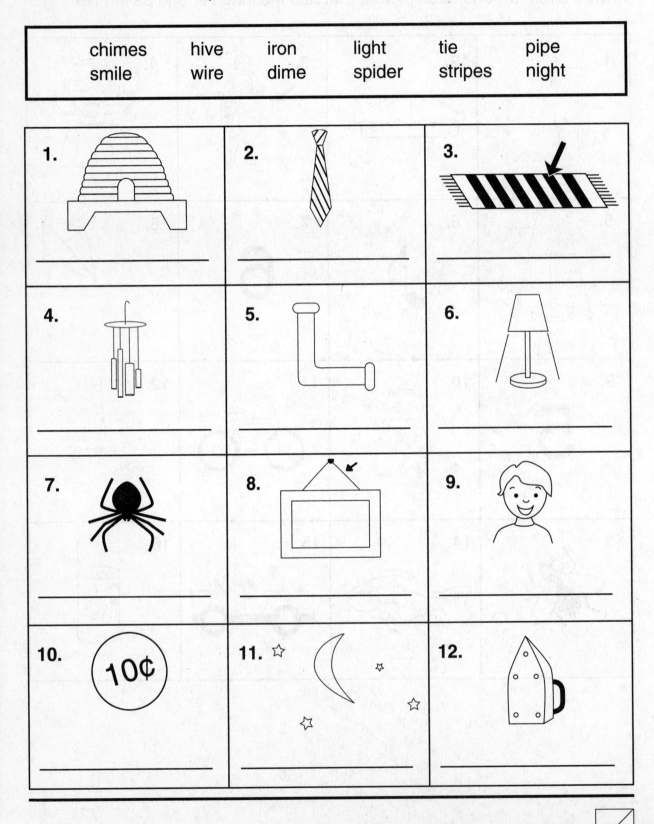

1. _____

2. _____

3. _____

4. _____

5. _____

6. _____

7. _____

8. _____

9. _____

10. _____

11. _____

12. _____

Long *i*

Draw a line to the word that answers each riddle. Then draw a circle around the letter or letters that stand for the vowel sound.

1. It is the opposite of *live*.

2. It is the opposite of *low*.

3. It is the opposite of *tame*.

4. It is the opposite of *truth*.

5. It is the opposite of *thin*.

6. It is the opposite of *frown*.

7. It is the opposite of *yours*.

8. It is the opposite of *groom*.

9. It is the opposite of *wet*.

10. It is the opposite of *day*.

wild

die

wide

bride

high

lie

dry

night

smile

mine

Long *i*

Find the word in the box that will finish each sentence. Write it on the line.

awhile	cry	miles	pine	pride
ride	side	smiled	strike	whined

1. Mike loved to _____ his horse, Spike.

2. They rode for _____ in the fields.

3. Mike liked to smell the _____ trees that were nearby.

4. Sometimes he would stop at the _____ of the brook.

5. He would let Spike drink and then rest _____.

6. One day Spike raised his front legs and _____.

7. A snake was ready to _____!

8. Mike knew he had to stay still and not _____ out.

9. Mike _____ as the snake slithered away.

10. That Spike is his _____ and joy!

Syllables

Name each picture. Draw a circle around the number of syllables you hear in the picture name.

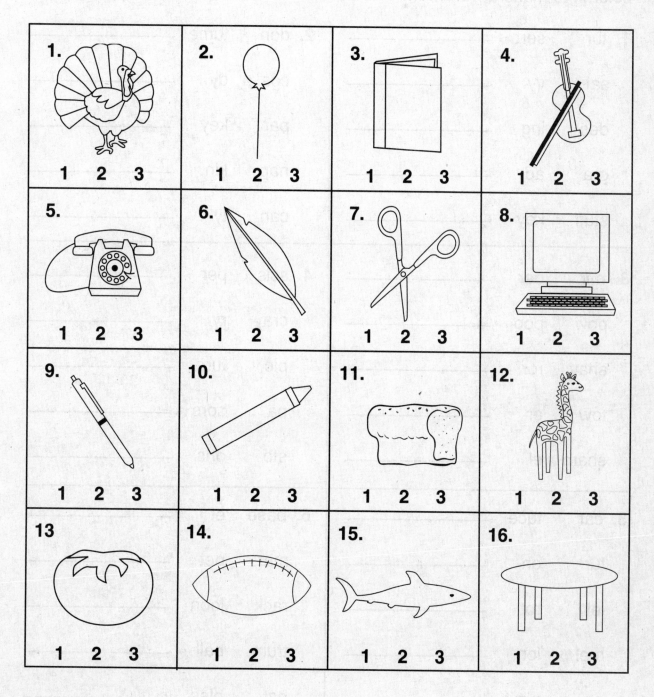

1.
1   2   3

2.
1   2   3

3.
1   2   3

4.
1   2   3

5.
1   2   3

6.
1   2   3

7.
1   2   3

8.
1   2   3

9.
1   2   3

10.
1   2   3

11.
1   2   3

12.
1   2   3

13
1   2   3

14.
1   2   3

15.
1   2   3

16.
1   2   3

Syllables

Draw a line from a syllable in the first column to a syllable in the second column to make a word. Write the word on the line.

1. tur   sert   _____

     sal   vy   _____

     des   ing   _____

     gra   ad   _____

     stuff   key   _____

2. don   tume   _____

     cos   dy   _____

     par   key   _____

     nap   kin   _____

     can   ty   _____

3. mir   der   _____

     pow   poo   _____

     shav   ror   _____

     tow   er   _____

     sham   el   _____

4. scis   per   _____

     cray   ry   _____

     pic   ture   _____

     pa   sors   _____

     sto   ons   _____

5. car   tuce   _____

     tur   on   _____

     let   rot   _____

     mel   ion   _____

     on   nip   _____

6. base   et   _____

     mar   pet   _____

     rack   loon   _____

     trum   ball   _____

     bal   bles   _____

Syllables

Draw a circle around the word that names the picture. Then write the word on the line, dividing it into syllables.

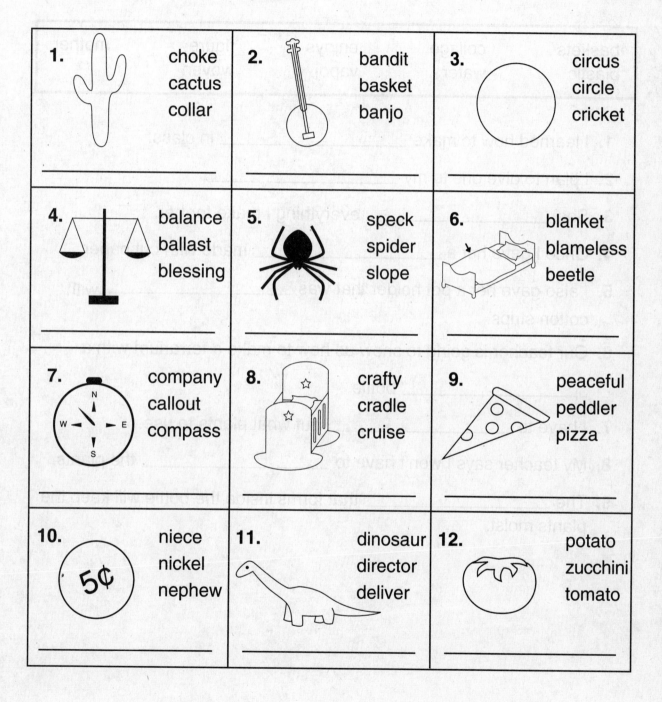

1. choke **cactus** collar	**2.** bandit basket **banjo**	**3.** **circus** circle cricket
4. **balance** ballast blessing	**5.** speck **spider** slope	**6.** **blanket** blameless beetle
7. company callout **compass**	**8.** crafty **cradle** cruise	**9.** peaceful peddler **pizza**
10. niece **nickel** nephew	**11.** **dinosaur** director deliver	**12.** potato zucchini **tomato**

Syllables

Find the word in the box that completes each sentence. Then write the
word on the line, dividing it into syllables.

baskets	collage	enjoys	figure	mother
plastic	water	vapor	woven	

1. I learned how to make _____ in class.

2. I plan to give one to my _____.

3. She _____ everything I make for her.

4. Once I gave her a _____ made with cut paper.

5. I also gave her a pot holder that was _____ with
   cotton strips.

6. Our teacher is going to show us how to make a terrarium with a
   _____ bottle.

7. I have to _____ out what plants to use.

8. My teacher says I won't have to _____ the plants.

9. The _____ that forms inside the bottle will keep the
   plants moist.

Review Long *a, i, e,* and Syllables

Find the name of each picture in the box. Write it on the line. Draw a circle around the letter or letters that stand for its vowel sound.

seat	light	cry	key	slide
rain	clay	flames	queen	

1. _____

2. _____

3. _____

4. _____

5. _____

6. _____

7. _____

8. _____

9. _____

Review Long *a, i, e,* and Syllables

Draw a circle around the letters that will finish the word in each sentence. Write the letters on the line.

1. I do not like to cl_____mb trees.   i   a   e   y

2. I do not like to be very h_____ up.   ie   igh   i

3. My friend, Joe, said I was too m_____k.   ea   ei   ee

4. I told Joe that he was w_____k.   ea   ei   ee

5. He could not lift a thirty pound w_____ght. ea   ei   ee

6. We have liked _____ch other for a long time. ea   ei   ee

7. We really never, ever f_____t.   ie   igh   i

8. We bel_____ve we will be friends as long as we live.   ie   igh   i

9. Now Joe is tr_____ing to get stronger.   i   a   e   y

10. And next w_____k, I'll make it up that tree! ea   ei   ee

Draw a line from a syllable in the first column to a syllable in the second column to make a word. Write the word on the line.

11. mil   ry   _____

12. yo   ey   _____

13. cher   vors   _____

14. mon   lion   _____

15. fla   gurt   _____

Review Long *a*, *i*, *e*, and Syllables

Look at each word in dark print. Write the letter or letters that stand for its long vowel sound on the line. Then draw a circle around the number that tells how many syllables are in the word.

1. **My** mother makes the best strudel. _____ 1 2 3

2. She uses big juicy apples and **raisins.** _____ 1 2 3

3. Her dough is always **light** and fluffy. _____ 1 2 3

4. I like to eat it with apple **cider.** _____ 1 2 3

5. Mom says dad **eats** too much strudel. _____ 1 2 3

6. He really has to watch his **diet.** _____ 1 2 3

7. Dad said he will **try** to cut back. _____ 1 2 3

8. He promised to give up **treats.** _____ 1 2 3

9. We want to **believe** him. _____ 1 2 3

10. We will just have to **wait** and see. _____ 1 2 3

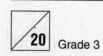

Review Long *a, i, e,* and Syllables

Read each clue. Find the answer in the word box. Write the word in the puzzle.

cry	dive	drive	flames	flight	niece	pain	paper
peace	please	retrieve	screech	shape	tires	weight	

Across

1. Fires cause these.
5. This is a polite word.
8. You do this when you are sad.
9. A car needs four of these.
10. Into the pool you go!
11. The opposite of war.
13. A sister's female child is this.

Down

1. This is a trip in an airplane.
2. A triangle is one kind.
3. You write on it.
4. You do this when you get a file on your computer.
6. This is an unpleasant noise.
7. To make a car go, you do this.
11. If you fall, you may feel this.
12. A scale helps tell you this.

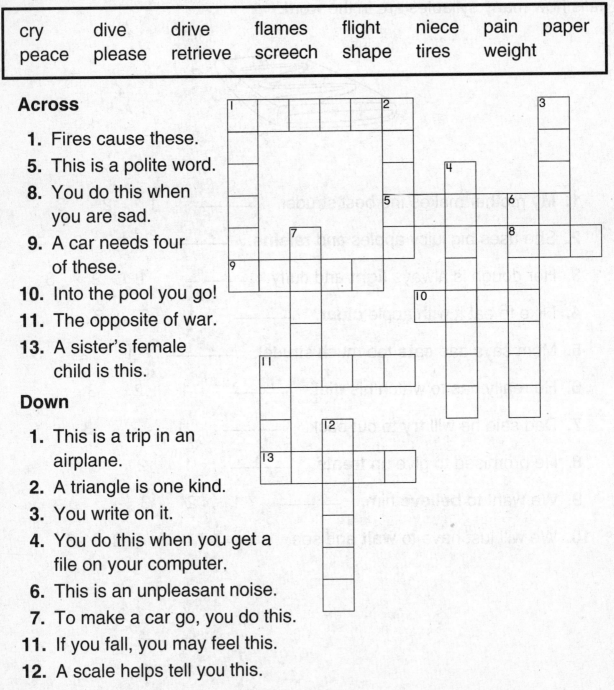

Read each clue again. Draw a circle around all the words that have two syllables. Underline words with three syllables.

Once a year, we sell some of the cattle at an auction. We use the money to buy grain for the animals, equipment, and food for us.

Dad promised me he will not sell my favorite pet pig which I call Pete. I bet you don't have a pet like that!

Please write again.

Your friend,
Jay

Dear Mike,

Living on a ranch in Oregon is so different from city life. I ride a bus for about an hour to get to school. There are only fifty kids in the whole school!

Fold the right side back on the long center line. Then fold the top half under the bottom half on the short center line. Cut open the tops of the pages.

Dear Jay,

I live in New York City where all kinds of unusual things happen. Right now a film company is making a movie at my neighbor's house.

Pen Pals

Every Thursday after school, I take a pottery class. I like to work with clay freehand, but I am also learning how to operate the potter's wheel.

Well, I have to do my math now. Please write soon.

Your Friend,
Mike

Before breakfast, I feed the pigs, sheep, and chickens. I also gather the eggs. Then I go in to eat. This morning I had pancakes and maple syrup.

After school, I ride my horse, Jeepers. We own 2,000 acres. I always look for any cattle that have roamed or strayed from the herd. We must keep count of our cattle.

I walk to school, just a few blocks away. My teacher was born in India, not too far from the Taj Mahal. She has taught us about some of her country's customs. She brought in a flat wheat bread called *chapati* for us to taste. Did you know that the cobra snake lives in India?

Last week, sparks flew from a manhole right outside my front window. We called the fire department who then called the electric company. A cable was broken, and if it hadn't been fixed, we could have had a blackout.

Listen for Long *o*

Name the pictures. Put an **X** on each picture that does not have the same vowel sound as in *boat*.

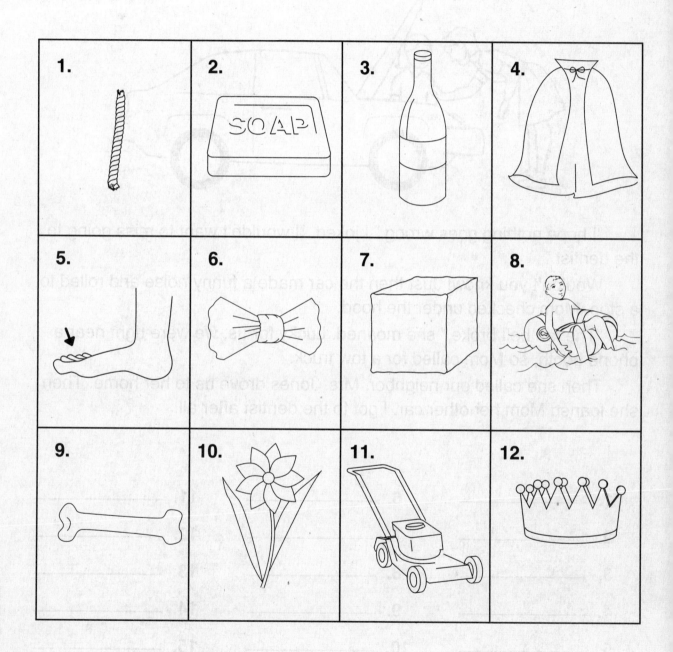

McGraw-Hill School Division

Long o

Read the story. Underline the words that have the same vowel sound as in *boat*. Then write those words on the lines.

"I hope nothing goes wrong," I joked. "I wouldn't want to miss going to the dentist."

Wouldn't you know! Just then the car made a funny noise and rolled to a stop. Mom checked under the hood.

"The fan belt broke," she moaned. Lucky for us, we were right near a phone booth, so Mom called for a tow truck.

Then she called our neighbor. Mrs. Jones drove us to her home. Then she loaned Mom her other car. I got to the dentist after all.

1. _____   6. _____   11. _____

2. _____   7. _____   12. _____

3. _____   8. _____   13. _____

4. _____   9. _____   14. _____

5. _____   10. _____   15. _____

Long o

In each sentence draw a circle around the word that has the same vowel sound as *boat*. Write the letters that stand for the sound.

1. When my dog gets loose, he likes to roam the neighborhood.
   _____

2. I guess the name Rover suits him. _____

3. Somehow he always finds his way home. _____

4. I just wish he didn't like to roll in the mud. _____

5. Sometimes his coat is just caked with it. _____

6. I wish I could get him to soak in a tub. _____

7. Instead, I have to hose him down. _____

8. Then I wash him until he's clean from tail to toe. _____

9. His fur is usually a deep gold. _____

10. He's not a show dog, but he is beautiful. _____

Long o

Draw a line to the word that answers each riddle.

1. This means "a female deer."

2. This means "to brag."

3. This is a bright color.

4. This has a pretty smell.

5. You might have this with eggs.

6. You use this tool in the garden.

7. You have this in soccer, hockey, and football.

8. This word means "an enemy."

9. This is the person who gives a party.

10. You send a secret message in this.

11. This is a young horse.

12. This is a rounded top on a building.

13. This means "to plant."

14. You have these in music.

15. Wood can do this, but rocks cannot.

yellow
rose
toast
doe
host
hoe
boast
code
notes
foe
goal
float
foal
sow
dome

McGraw-Hill School Division

Name_____ Date_____

Listen for Long *u*

Name the pictures. Underline the pictures that do not have the same vowel sound as in *blew* or *fuse*.

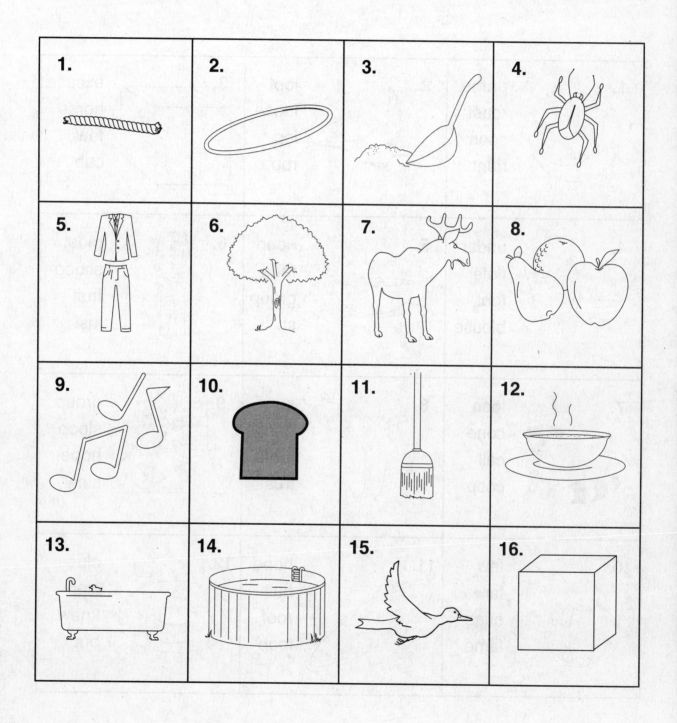

McGraw-Hill School Division

Long *u*

Draw a circle around each word that has the same vowel sound as the name of the picture.

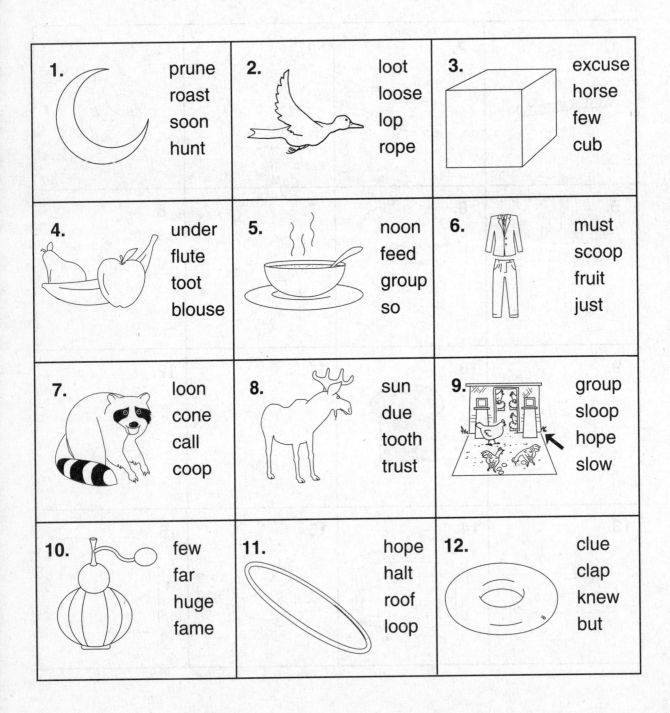

1. prune roast soon hunt	**2.** loot loose lop rope	**3.** excuse horse few cub
4. under flute toot blouse	**5.** noon feed group so	**6.** must scoop fruit just
7. loon cone call coop	**8.** sun due tooth trust	**9.** group sloop hope slow
10. few far huge fame	**11.** hope halt roof loop	**12.** clue clap knew but

Long *u*

Draw a line to the word that answers each riddle. Then underline the letters that stand for the long *u* sound.

1. This is one serving of ice cream.

2. This word means "sleep."

3. This means "to save or set free."

4. This fruit is a dried plum.

5. This word means "very, very large."

6. You are one.

7. It has six sides.

8. You can whistle this.

9. This means "being young."

10. You pay this to a club.

11. This is a kind of water bird.

12. A group of people who work together on a job.

13. This clever animal wears a mask.

14. You can sit on this small round seat.

15. It is not a lie.

rescue

prune

tune

scoop

dues

snooze

loon

huge

human

crew

cube

raccoon

stool

truth

youth

Long *u*

Find the word in the box that will finish each sentence. Write it on the line.

troop	use	amuse	moose	excuse
museum	choose	huge	soup	few

1. Rudy's scout _____ really likes to camp out.

2. They find any _____ to cook over a fire.

3. One thing they make really well is chicken _____.

4. They always _____ fresh vegetables.

5. There are _____ people who can resist their muffins, too.

6. Aunt Lucy took me to the _____ last week.

7. We saw a painting of a _____.

8. Did you know the moose is a _____ animal?

9. After, Aunt Lucy let me _____ something from the museum shop.

10. I picked a stuffed toy kangaroo, because they always

_____ me.

McGraw-Hill School Division

Listen for Diphthongs

Draw a circle around the pictures whose names have the same vowel sound as in *boy*.

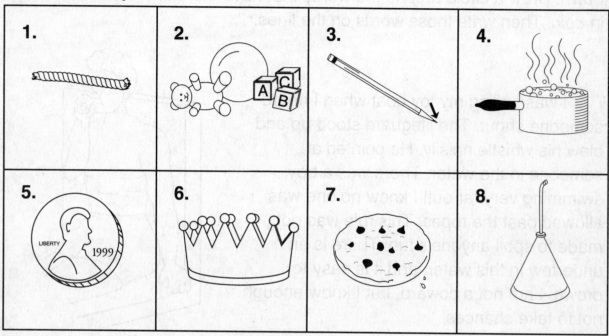

Draw a circle around the pictures whose names have the same vowel sound as in *crown*.

Diphthongs

Read the story. Underline the words that have the same vowel sound as in *down*. Draw a circle around the words that have the same vowel sound as in *coin*. Then write those words on the lines.

I was sailing my toy boat when I heard someone shout. The lifeguard stood up and blew his whistle noisily. He pointed at someone in the water. There was a boy swimming very far out! I knew no one was allowed past the ropes. This rule was not made to spoil anyone's fun. There is an undertow in this water, and it is easy to drown. I am not a coward, but I know enough not to take chances.

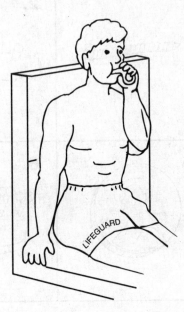

sound as in *down*   sound as in *coin*

_____   _____

_____   _____

_____   _____

_____   _____

Diphthongs

Draw a circle around each word that has the same vowel sound as the name of the picture.

1. coast royal enjoy hope	**2.** loot pounce allow poem	**3.** join loyal robe you
4. joy flower power group	**5.** coop point joy paint	**6.** tower flour roof royal
7. toil trout flour boost	**8.** avoid round oyster throw	**9.** brown moist choice found
10. now close noise house	**11.** mount booth outer slow	**12.** foil count bound hoist

Diphthongs

Draw a line to the word that answers each riddle. Then underline the letters that stand for the vowel sound.

1. This is something that can make you ill.

2. This word means "force" or "might."

3. This is the opposite of *quiet*.

4. If you go by ship, you are taking this.

5. It means "to have a good time."

6. He might wear a rubber nose and a wig.

7. This is the opposite of *lost*.

8. You can wrap this around a sandwich to keep it fresh.

9. This can mean a high-ranking nobleman.

10. If you can take your pick, you have this.

11. Friends should be this.

12. If you do this you will be noisy.

13. This means the same as "give permission."

14. If you leave milk out on a warm day, it will do this.

15. A cat does this to catch a mouse.

power

shout

clown

poison

noisy

enjoy

count

voyage

choice

found

foil

spoil

pounce

loyal

allow

Grade 3   15

McGraw-Hill School Division

Compound Words

Find the name of each picture in the box. Write it on the line.

birdhouse	mailbox	doghouse	armchair	earthworm	flagpole
postcard	snowman	fingernail	blackberry	paintbrush	
raincoat	waterfall	suitcase	scarecrow	snowflake	

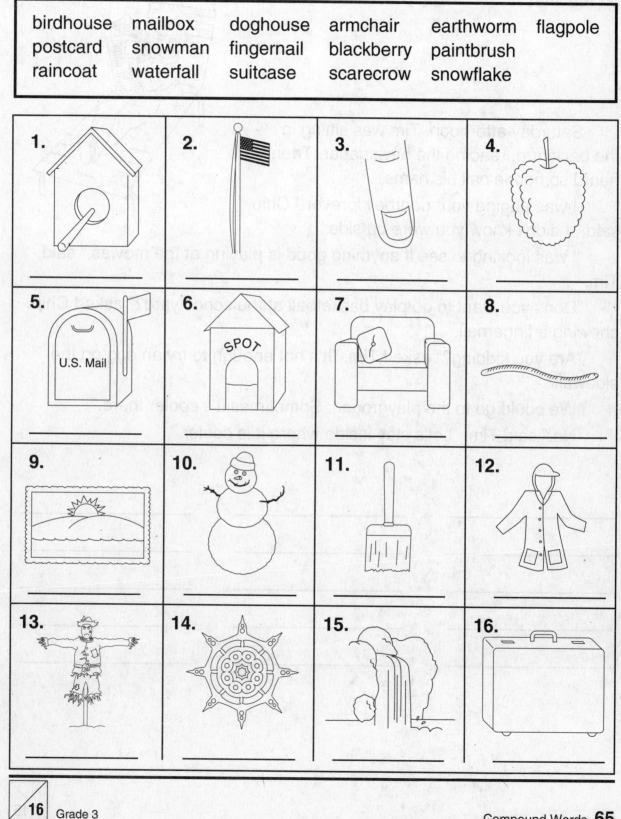

1. _____

2. _____

3. _____

4. _____

5. _____

6. _____

7. _____

8. _____

9. _____

10. _____

11. _____

12. _____

13. _____

14. _____

15. _____

16. _____

Compound Words

Read the story. Underline the compound words. Write those words on the lines.

     Saturday afternoon, Tim was sitting in the backyard, reading the newspaper. Then he heard someone call his name.

     "I was ringing your doorbell forever!" Chip said. "I didn't know you were outside."

     "I was looking to see if anything good is playing at the movies," said Tim.

     "Don't you want to go play basketball at the schoolyard?" asked Chip, chewing a fingernail.

     "Are you kidding?" asked Tim. "It's hot enough to fry an egg on the sidewalk."

     "We could go to the playground. Sometimes it's cooler there."

     "No," said Tim. "Let's stay inside where it is cooler."

_____   _____   _____

_____   _____   _____

_____   _____   _____

_____   _____   _____

_____   _____   _____

Compound Words

Find the word in the box that will finish each sentence. Write it on the line.

flagpole	waterfall	suitcase	backpack	flashlight
lunchtime	campfire	overnight	bunkbeds	moonlight

1. I will never forget my first _____ camping trip.

2. I carried my clothes in my_____.

3. We arrived at camp just at _____.

4. After lunch, we took a hike to a lake with a _____.

5. I was glad I had my bathing suit in my _____.

6. At night we cooked hot dogs and sang songs around a

   _____.

7. The full moon was so bright, you could almost read by the

   _____.

8. Then we went back to the cabin and slept in _____.

9. There were no lights in the cabin. I was glad I had brought my

   _____.

10. In the morning we had assembly around the _____.

Compound Words

Read each clue. Find the answer in the word box. Write the word in the puzzle.

postcard	cardboard	newspaper	raincoat	paperboy	daylight
footprint	fingerprint	barnyard	playmate	notebook	railroads

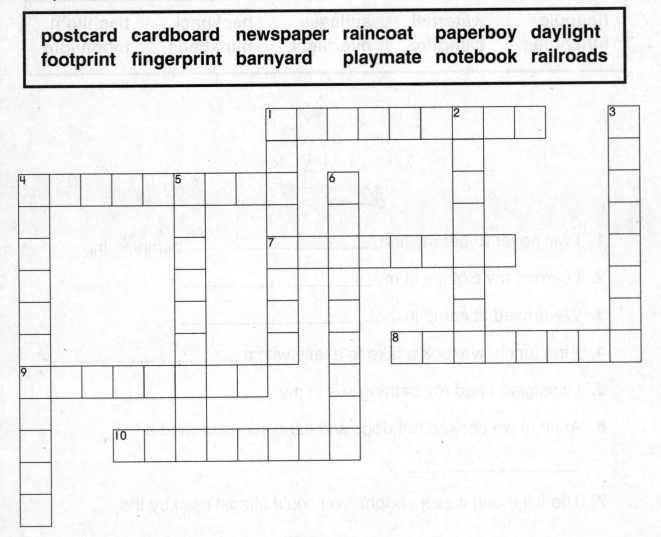

Across

1. A paper that has the news.
4. The mark your foot makes.
7. The yard just outside a barn.
8. The light during the day.
9. Someone to play with.
10. A small card you can send.

Down

1. A book to take notes in.
2. The boy who brings the paper.
3. Something to wear in the rain.
4. The mark your finger makes.
5. These make you think of trains.
6. Boxes are often made of this.

Syllables

Draw a circle around the word that names the picture. Then write the word on the line, dividing it into syllables.

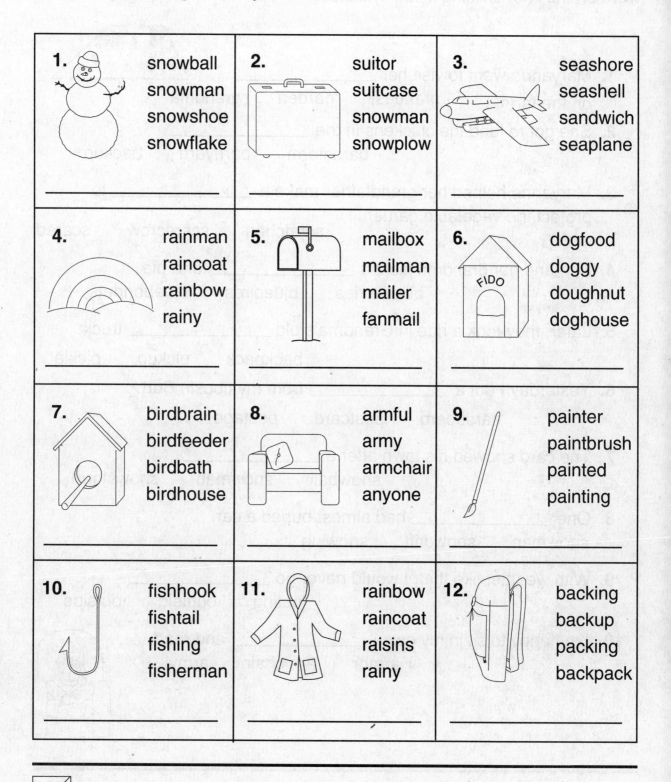

1. snowball
   snowman
   snowshoe
   snowflake

   _____

2. suitor
   suitcase
   snowman
   snowplow

   _____

3. seashore
   seashell
   sandwich
   seaplane

   _____

4. rainman
   raincoat
   rainbow
   rainy

   _____

5. mailbox
   mailman
   mailer
   fanmail

   _____

6. dogfood
   doggy
   doughnut
   doghouse

   _____

7. birdbrain
   birdfeeder
   birdbath
   birdhouse

   _____

8. armful
   army
   armchair
   anyone

   _____

9. painter
   paintbrush
   painted
   painting

   _____

10. fishhook
    fishtail
    fishing
    fisherman

    _____

11. rainbow
    raincoat
    raisins
    rainy

    _____

12. backing
    backup
    packing
    backpack

    _____

Syllables

Draw a circle around the word that finishes each sentence. Then write the word on the line, dividing it into syllables.

1. Maryanne went to visit her _____ on the farm.

   grandest   garden   grandma

2. She got to feed the chickens in the _____.

   barnstorm   barnyard   backup

3. Maryanne helped her grandfather make a _____ to protect the vegetable garden.

   scratches   scarecrow   scared

4. She and her grandma picked _____ for a pie.

   blueberries   bluebirds   bluebonnets

5. Later, they took a ride in Grandma's old _____ truck.

   backpack   pickup   pickle

6. Yesterday I got a _____ from my cousin Burt.

   cardboard   postcard   postage

7. The card showed his town after a _____.

   snowball   snowman   snowstorm

8. One _____ had almost buried a car.

   snowman   snowdrift   snowing

9. With weather like that, I would never go _____.

   outing   outfield   outside

10. I'm happy to sit in my cozy _____ and read.

    armor   armchair   army

McGraw-Hill School Division

Review Long *o, u*, Diphthongs, Compound Words

Draw a circle around each word that has the same vowel sound as the name of the picture.

1. boat
choice
fruit
few

suitcase

2. glow
goal
group
moose

goose

3. house
hoop
flour
hoist

scout

4. rope
moon
fold
mouse

toast

5. flower
roast
broil
go

snowman

6. boy
crown
look
pout

loudspeaker

7. coat
sound
doughnut
found

doghouse

8. storm
coast
blow
cow

mower

9. troop
footprint
soon
moist

moon

10. slow
hope
found
pounce

doe

11. coat
hoe
broom
suit

toenail

12. blew
stew
float
fold

fruit

Review Long *o, u,* Diphthongs, Compound Words

Draw a line to the word that answers each riddle.

1. This is a high place where you could ski or hike.

2. This is where you go to learn.

3. Your pencil won't write without this.

4. A hard rainstorm can be called this.

5. This makes the ground shake.

6. This means the same as "spoil."

7. This means "to stay away from."

8. Something that is a fact is this.

9. This word means "hard work."

10. This word describes kings and queens.

11. Put this in your garden to scare the birds.

12. This is money you get every week.

13. This means "to plant seeds."

14. You have these above your eyes.

15. This is a sport you play with a ball and pins.

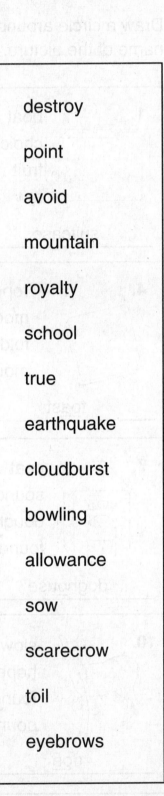

destroy

point

avoid

mountain

royalty

school

true

earthquake

cloudburst

bowling

allowance

sow

scarecrow

toil

eyebrows

Review Long *o, u*, Diphthongs, Compound Words

Read the sentences. Underline the words that have the same vowel sound as in *boat.* Draw a circle around the words that have the same vowel sound as *moon* or *fuse.*

1. I was hoeing weeds in my garden when I saw a small yellow bird.

2. It landed on my scarecrow's coat.

3. To tell you the truth, I knew that thing was useless.

4. "Friend or foe?" I asked the bird.

5. Without a sound, he flew away.

Underline the words that have the same vowel sound as in *boy.* Draw a circle around the words that have the same vowel sound as *out.*

6. What is the choice for lunch today?

7. You can have trout or broiled flounder.

8. There is crown roast with brown gravy.

9. You can have boiled potatoes, too.

10. I avoid eating anything with soy sauce.

Review Long *o*, Long *u*, Diphthongs, Compound Words

Underline the compound words. Then write those words on the lines, dividing them into syllables.

1. I cleaned my bedroom yesterday.
2. I found a toy cowboy without his horse, and a baseball cap.
3. I found my paintbox and sketchpad, too.
4. I couldn't find my paintbrush anywhere.
5. Someday I will empty my backpack, too.

1. _____ 2. _____

3. _____ 4. _____

5. _____ 6. _____

7. _____ 8. _____

9. _____ 10. _____

Draw a line from a word in the first column to a word in the second column to make a compound word. Write the word on the line.

1. snow	beam	2. dog	ball	3. some	time
paint	man	bird	yard	every	light
sun	light	barn	house	any	one
moon	brush	base	bath	day	where

_____ _____ _____

_____ _____ _____

_____ _____ _____

_____ _____ _____

_____

Joan and Joyce started making a wall. But the wall kept falling down.

"This snow is powder," said Joan. "It isn't good for packing."

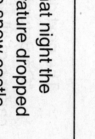

"Maybe we could use wood for supports and then cover the wood with snow," said Roy.

Mrs. Lloyd checked the rule book. "It says sculptures must be made of only snow or ice."

That night the temperature dropped and the snow castle was covered with a thin coating of ice. It seemed to glow in the moonlight.

At the contest site we found a trophy on our castle. "First prize - Snow Castle - Mrs. Lloyd's third grade!"

Fold the right side back on the long center line. Then fold the top half under the bottom half on the short center line. Cut open the tops of the pages.

The Snow Castle

"Look at this poster for the Winter Fest," said Joyce.

"There's going to be a contest this year for the best snow sculpture."

"Cool!" said Luke. "Let's enter it."

"Let's get our whole class to help," said Joan.

"How should we build it?" asked Mrs. Lloyd. "We want it to be strong."

"Let's practice at lunch time," suggested Joan.

So we all ate quickly and then went out to the field behind the school. Luckily there had been a snowstorm just two days before, and there was plenty of fresh snow. It would stay, too, because the forecast was for the weather to stay cold.

The Winter Fest is the festival our town of Mount Royal puts on every year in February. There are snowmobile races, snowmen building contests, an ice skating show, and all sorts of stuff. It helps people get rid of the winter blues.

Mrs. Lloyd, our teacher, was excited when we told her. "Let's hear ideas for what we can make," she said.

"A snow family," said Roy.

"A polar bear," said Sue.

"A huge snow fort with towers and a moat," said Luke.

"Yeah!" shouted everyone. "That's the best idea of all."

6

That night, Luke was setting the table. He went to the freezer to get ice cubes. Suddenly the ice cube tray gave him an idea!

The next day he told everyone his idea. "On Saturday everyone must bring milk cartons of all sizes. We will make snow bricks!"

Everyone brought their milk cartons to the contest site. We filled them with snow and packed it down as hard as we could. When we turned the cartons over, we had snow bricks.

We built a wonderful snow castle. It had a tower with a flight of stairs to the top and a moat all around it. When we were all done, we sprayed the whole castle lightly with water.

The Snow Castle McGraw-Hill School Division

Listen for R-controlled Vowels

Draw a circle around the pictures in each row whose names have the same
vowel sound.

R-controlled Vowels *ar, ir, or, ur, er*

Find the word in the box that will finish each sentence. Write it on the line.

bear	birthday	cheered	for	form
girl	hairbrush	purse	stars	years

I am one happy _____! Today is my

_____. I am ten-_____-old.

One of my gifts was a new leather _____.

I jumped up and _____ when I got it. I have wanted one

_____ such a long time. I put my _____

and my comb in it. I also put in my tiny little teddy_____

and my fun stickers of blue and red _____.

I had to fill out a _____ for school,

so I put that in too.

Draw a circle around the letters that will finish the word in each sentence.
Write the letters on the line.

1. I am so mis_____able with this bad cold and
   high fever.   ir   er   or

2. I am going to miss our school's spring conc_____t.   ir   er   or

3. I play the violin in the _____chestra.   ir   er   or

4. My music teacher said I make the strings ch_____p
   like a bird.   ir   er   or

5. She said that everyone will miss seeing my
   perf_____mance.   ir   er   or

R-controlled Vowels *ar, ir, or, ur, er*

Draw a line to the word that answers each riddle. Then draw a circle around the letters **ar, ir, or, ur,** and **er** in the word.

1. It means to get ready.

2. Your heart is one.

3. This is the opposite of *lightness.*

4. Elephants travel in these.

5. This is the opposite of *funny.*

6. This is a natural disaster.

7. This is another word for *gigantic.*

8. If you are not wrong, you are ————.

9. Your face may turn red if you are this.

10. This is a show with clowns and
    acrobats.

11. You use this to plug a bottle.

12. You want this when you watch a game.

13. If you twist about you do this.

14. You need this for your living room.

15. Red, blue, red, blue, red, blue is
    one kind.

darkness
serious
prepare
earthquake
enormous
organ
circus
cork
squirm
score
furniture
pattern
correct
embarrassed
herds

McGraw-Hill School Division

R-controlled Vowels *ar, ir, or, ur, er*

Read the story. Write the underlined words on the lines below. Then draw a circle around the letters that stand for the vowel sound.

My teacher showed us a film about the Statue of Liberty.

She told us that we are going to visit it on Thursday, February 10th. She wanted our class to be well informed. So off we went to the library to learn more about the lady in New York Harbor.

The lady is located on Liberty Island. She is a symbol of freedom. In her right hand, she holds a torch that stands for liberty. Her left hand holds a tablet with the date July 4, 1776 on it. This was the day that the U.S. declared its freedom from Great Britain. The lady wears a flowing robe and a spiked crown with seven rays. The spikes stand for the world's seven seas and continents.

The surface of the statue is made of copper sheets that are attached to an iron frame. The frame was made by the French engineer Gustave Alexandre Eiffel. He also built the Eiffel Tower in Paris.

1. _____

2. _____

3. _____

4. _____

5. _____

6. _____

7. _____

8. _____

9. _____

10. _____

11. _____

12. _____

13. _____

14. _____

15. _____

Silent Letters *k, w, l, b, gh*

Say the name of each picture. Then draw a circle around the silent letter or letters.

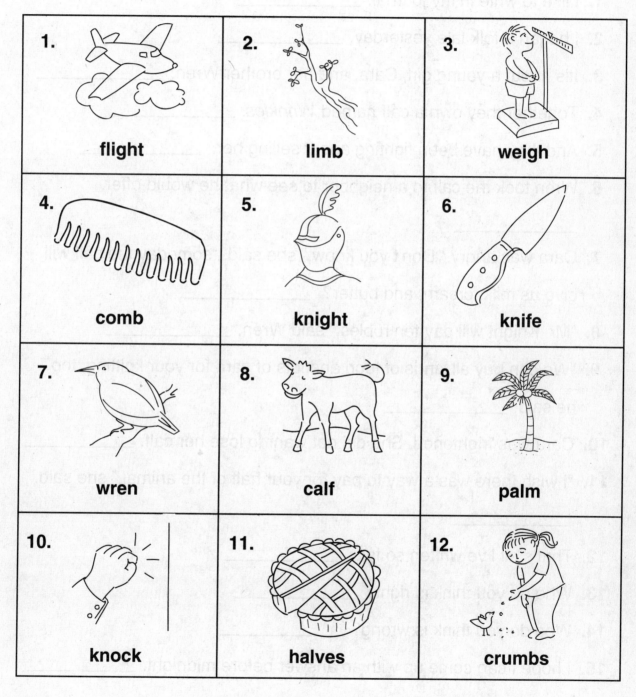

1. flight	2. limb	3. weigh
4. comb	5. knight	6. knife
7. wren	8. calf	9. palm
10. knock	11. halves	12. crumbs

Silent Letters *k, w, l, b, gh*

Underline the word or words with the silent letter or letters in each sentence. Then write the letter(s) on the line.

1. I like to write in my journal. _____

2. I began a folk tale yesterday. _____

3. It's about a young girl, Cara, and her brother Wren. _____

4. Together they own a calf named *Wrinkles*. _____

5. And they have been fighting about selling her. _____

6. Wren took the calf to a neighbor to see what he would offer.

_____

7. Cara was angry. "Don't you know," she said, "someday the calf will

give us milk, cream, and butter?" _____

8. "Mr. Knight will pay ten rubles," said Wren. _____

9. "We can buy all kinds of food and lots of yarn for your knitting, too."

he said. _____

10. Cara was frightened. She did not want to lose her calf. _____

11. "I wish there was a way to pay for your half of the animal," she said.

_____

12. That's all I've written so far. _____

13. Who do you think is right? _____

14. Who do you think is wrong? _____

15. I hope I can come up with an answer before midnight. _____

Silent Letters *k, w, l, b, gh*

Find a word in the box to finish each sentence. Write it on the line. Then draw a circle around the silent letter(s).

comb	flight	folks	height	knees
knit	knock	limbs	neighborhood	palm
right	sightseeing	weigh	write	written

1. Have you ever counted the lines in the _____ of your hand?

2. How many pounds do you _____?

3. What is your _____ in feet and inches?

4. Can you touch your toes without bending your _____?

5. Do you brush or _____ your hair?

6. Are your arms and other _____ as long as your Mom's?

7. Can you _____ a scarf or a hat?

8. Did you ever take a _____ on a jet?

9. Have you ever gone _____ in a new city?

10. Can you name five stores in your _____?

11. Have you ever _____ a letter to the editor of a newspaper?

12. Do you know where your _____ were born?

13. How many _____ turns do you take coming to school?

14. Do you like to _____ stories?

15. Do you like to tell _____-knock jokes?

Silent Letters

Draw a line to the word that answers each riddle. Then draw a circle around the silent letter or letters.

1. This is a kind of tree.

2. Maple and other trees have these.

3. If you divide a pie in two pieces, you have this.

4. This is part of the back of your leg.

5. This is a young sheep.

6. The opposite of a curved line is a _____ line.

7. This is when owls can't see very well.

8. This is something used to cut things.

9. This is the opposite of *dull*.

10. Someone who wore armor.

11. Something that is not in pieces.

12. This is another word for *strong*.

13. You might use this in cooking.

14. This is someone who can fix a leaky pipe.

15. You put this on a present.

half
lamb
palm
daylight
limbs
bright
calf
whole
breadcrumbs
knife
straight
knight
wrapping
mighty
plumber

Soft *c* and Soft *g*

Underline the pictures whose names have the soft **c** or soft **g** sound.

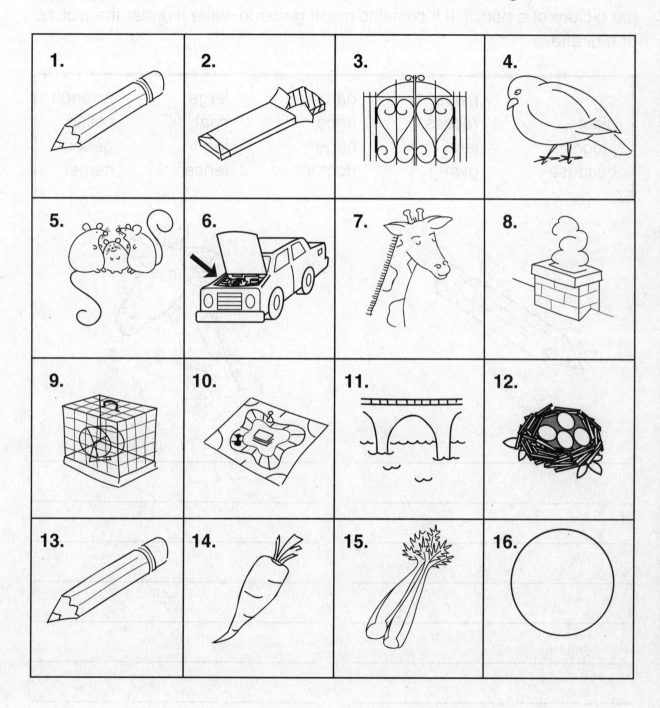

1.

2.

3.

4.

5.

6.

7.

8.

9.

10.

11.

12.

13.

14.

15.

16.

Soft *c* and Soft *g*

Say each word in the box below. If it contains a soft **c** sound, write it under the picture of a pencil. If it contains a soft **g** sound, write it under the picture of a giraffe.

city	place	garden	large	arrange
giant	recess	price	coat	cellar
judge	lace	huge	leg	general
because	gym	doctor	fence	center

_____

_____

_____

_____

_____

_____

Soft *c* and Soft *g*

Draw a line to the word that answers each riddle. Then draw a circle around the letters that stand for the soft **c** or soft **g** sound.

1. This is the last month of the year.

2. This is where a king lives.

3. This is frozen water.

4. People are buried here.

5. The year 2000 begins a new _____.

6. This is a juicy fruit.

7. This is the opposite of small.

8. This is a kind of dinosaur.

9. A book has these.

10. This animal has a long neck.

cemetery

tangerine

ice

pages

triceratops

December

palace

large

century

giraffe

Soft *c* and Soft *g*

Find the word in the box that will finish each sentence. Write it on the line and draw a circle around the letters that stand for the soft **c** or soft **g** sounds.

cents	cereal	charges	face	judge
center	ranger	sentence	service	since

Goldilocks was brought before the _____ last

Tuesday afternoon. He told her that the three bears were unhappy. "They

have brought four _____ against you," he said. "First, you

broke into their house. That is unlawful. Second, you ate their

_____, which means you stole it. And third, you broke

baby bear's chair. So you destroyed property."

"How do you plead?" asked the judge.

"I did do all those things," said Goldilocks, her head low.

"_____ you have admitted your crimes," said the

judge, "I will be lenient."

"Now, Goldilocks," said the judge, "it is time for your

_____. A new chair costs five dollars and fifty

_____. You must buy a new one for little bear. Then

you must do some community _____. You will work in the

_____ with the park _____ and help her

watch out for animal traps and campfires."

"I am so sorry for all the trouble," Goldilocks said with a sad

_____. "I will never enter the bears' house without being

asked."

And she never did!

McGraw-Hill School Division

Vowels /u̇/, /ô/

Draw a circle around all the pictures whose names have the same vowel sound as in *foot*.

1.	2.	3.	4.
5.	6.	7.	8.

Draw a circle around all the pictures that have the same vowel sound as in *saucer*.

9.	10.	11.	12.
13.	14.	15.	16.

 16 Grade 3

Vowels /ů/, /ô/

Complete each word using the letters in the box. Then write the words on the lines under the correct sound.

a	o	au	ough	oo	u

I went shopping at the m_____ll yesterday. I w_____lked for hours looking

at all the g_____ds. I _____lmost b_____t a new w_____len sweater at one

store. I got a cupf_____l of hot chocolate and a c_____kie at another. I

spent a lot of time in the b_____kstore and t_____lked with the owner

about some new posters.

     Then I found a l_____st child. I knew she was someone's d_____ghter

and I had to find her parent. I looked down the h_____ll for a police officer.

But then a frantic w_____man came running toward us. Once she hugged

her child and realized she was fine, she scolded her. "You n_____ghty girl!

Why didn't you stay by my side?" "It's not my f_____ult!" cried the girl. You

lost me! The mother smiled and sh_____k my hand. She thanked me for

being so kind.

/ô/ (saucer)   **/ů/ (foot)**

_____   _____

_____   _____

_____   _____

_____   _____

Vowels /ů/, /ô/

Draw a line to the word that answers each riddle. Then draw a circle around the letter or letters that stand for the /ô/ or /ů/ sound.

1. This is the sound a dog might make.

2. This is an idea.

3. People keep money and jewels here.

4. You might see these in the snow.

5. This bird has a strong beak.

6. You'll see this around a fireplace.

7. This is the opposite of short.

8. This is a short break in time.

9. This is the eighth month of the year.

10. It comes in cubes and powder too.

11. This helps you keep your place.

12. This is a sweet dessert.

13. This means many times.

14. You do this when you pull or drag something.

15. This helps raise the flag.

footprints

woodpecker

soot

woof

thought

August

vault

tall

pudding

often

pause

pulley

bookmark

sugar

haul

Vowels /u̇/, /ô/

Find the word in the box that best tells about each picture. Write it on the line. Then draw a circle around all the words that have the same vowel sound as *saucer*.

cook	daughter	fall	footprints	full	shook
soft	song	waterfall	woman	woodchuck	wool

1.

2.

3.

4.

5.

6.

7.

8.

9.

10.

11.

12.

Review R-controlled Vowels, Silent Letters, Soft *g* and Soft *c* and Variant Vowels

Draw a circle around the word that has the same vowel sound, soft *g* or soft *c* sound, or silent letter as the name of the picture.

1. sorting nearing breaking curing **beard**	**2.** job dream face kitten **rice**	**3.** sharp square merchant torn **turtle**
4. write crook daughter hoping **wolf**	**5.** come carry crumb crab **comb**	**6.** charms maybe hares music **markers**
7. digging grown engine glass **giraffe**	**8.** guess pledge test garden **judge**	**9.** bought bookmark flavor sample **saucer**
10. rage alarm city crease **circle**	**11.** kind kettle knit kick **knock**	**12.** cookie shore food cents **core**

Review R-controlled Vowels, Silent Letters, Soft *g* and Soft *c* and Variant Vowels

Draw lines to connect the words that have the same sounds.

1. engineer

2. important

3. hair

4. fudge

5. skirt

6. ginger

7. sister

8. autumn

9. woman

10. city

grudge

giraffe

caught

deer

storm

cents

chair

bird

summer

book

Read each sentence and underline the words that have silent letters. Then draw a circle around the silent letters.

From my bedroom window I sometimes hear thunder and see lightning streak across the sky. My palms sweat. My limbs freeze. My whole body is tense. But then there is a knock at the door. I hear my folks say, "Don't be frightened. Everyone is all right. The storm will be over by daylight. Sleep tight."

Review R-controlled Vowels, Silent Letters, Soft *g* and Soft *c* and Variant Vowels

Find a word in the box to complete each sentence. Write it on the line.

curtain	looked	giant	gym	knew	learned
once	perform	scared	scenery	smart	song
star	startled	stood	stage	words	wrote

Our school doesn't have an auditorium so we

put on plays in the _____. The

_____, where we act, is at one end.

Some sliding doors serve as a _____.

Our class _____ a play about a mean

tall _____ and a slow but very _____ turtle. I

was the giant. I had _____ all my lines. I really

_____ them all. But when it was my turn to _____,

I was so _____. I just _____ there and I

_____ at the audience.

Then a tree in the background _____ fell and

_____ me. All of a sudden the _____ came. I

didn't make a mistake, not even _____. Soon it was time for

everyone to sing a _____.

My Dad said I was the _____ of the show.

Review R-controlled Vowels, Silent Letters, Soft g and Soft c and Variant Vowels

Use words from the box to complete the puzzle. Then read the shaded boxes to find out who the secret person is.

cage	chair	circle	engineer	hair	high	June
knit	light	market	mice	naughty	near	right
search	shirt	turtle	voice	world	wren	

1. You do this to make a sweater.
2. This is a bird.
3. Opposite of dark is __.
4. A bird is inside this __.
5. Opposite of low is __.
6. You wear this.
7. It's a round shape.
8. Opposite of far is __.
9. You sit on it.
10. You may shop here.
11. They like cheese.
12. A globe shows this.
13. Its house is a shell.

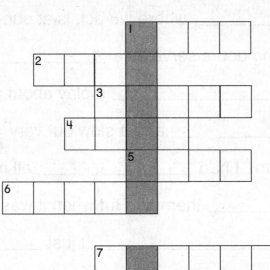

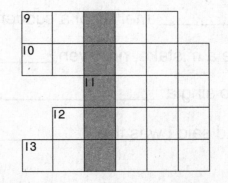

There are many other common birds, such as the robin, the cardinal, the wren, and the warbler. There are some water birds too, such as the goose, the duck, and the swan. Maybe you would like to read about them and share your information with the class.

Fold the right side back on the long center line. Then fold the top half under the bottom half on the short center line. Cut open the tops of the pages.

Another common bird is the crow. Some crows migrate, but many stay around for the winter. Crows eat eggs, young birds, and other small animals, vegetable matter, and garbage. If there is a lot of food around, the crow will hide it away to use in winter months—just like a squirrel! Many farmers consider the crow a big pest! Can you guess why the scarecrow was invented?

Birds Around You

No matter where you live, in the city or the country, you hear or see some type of bird almost every day.

Knock, knock, knock! Is that a woodpecker pecking a hole in a tree in your backyard? It may be drilling a hole to nest in or to find some yummy insects to eat. One kind of woodpecker is called a sapsucker because it drills small holes in the sides of the trees and draws out sap with its long brush-tipped tongue.

7

Another common bird is the barn owl, the only owl that lives in the United States. Barn owls have a heart-shaped face, rather than the circular one of other owls. Barn owls hunt at night. They eat mostly small mammals. They nest in hollow trees, barns, belfries, and other nooks. They usually lay five to seven chalky white eggs. Listen for their nighttime song. "Who-o-o-o, who-o-o-o!"

Birds Around You McGraw-Hill School Division

One common bird is the pigeon. These birds have small heads, short necks, and stout bodies. They nest in trees, on the ground, or any cozy nook they happen upon. They eat seeds, fruits, acorns, and other nuts. They build loose, almost flat nests of twigs, bark, straw, and weeds. The female lays one or two tan or white eggs.

The homing pigeon is trained to return to its loft or cage. It is not fully understood how the pigeon can travel far, far from its home and still find its way back. Scientists believe that these pigeons rely on the light patterns in the sky, the magnetic field of earth, and various landmarks.

Vowels /ər/ er; /ən/ en; /əl/ le

Draw a line from a syllable in the first column to a syllable in the second column to make a word. Write the word on the line.

hap	dle	nim	den	rip	er	can	en
play	en	fid	der	talk	en	mid	ble
wood	pen	thun	dle	thim	ple	sharp	dle
han	er	sud	ble	tight	ble	hum	dle

_____ _____ _____ _____

_____ _____ _____ _____

_____ _____ _____ _____

Now use words on the lines to finish the sentences in the story below.

The next man to play was Pat. There was a small _____ of applause. He picked up his fiddle by the _____ and walked to the _____ of the room. He plucked some strings and listened. Then I saw him loosen some strings and _____ others. Finally he put the _____ under his chin and began to play a lively reel. Then all of a _____, he played faster and faster. Finally, he finished. The applause sounded like _____ . Pat smiled shyly. He may be a _____ man, but he is the best fiddle _____ I have ever heard.

McGraw-Hill School Division

Vowels /ər/er; /ən/en; /əl/le

Find the word in the box that goes with each picture. Write the word on the line, dividing it into syllables.

thimble	sprinkle	handle	table
whistle	rattle	crumble	bottle

1. _____

2. _____

3. _____

4. _____

5. _____

6. _____

7. _____

8. _____

Draw a circle around the word that completes each sentence. Then write the word on the line, dividing it into syllables.

1. How did Tim _____ to try out for the play?

happy   happen   sharpen

2. He has always wanted to be an _____.

acted   acting   actor

3. Being on a stage doesn't _____ him at all.

fighter   frighten   fright

4. I can feel my heartbeat _____ just thinking about speaking in front of a hundred people.

quicken   quickly   quickest

5. I am meant to be a _____, not an actor.

written   writing   writer

Contractions

Draw a circle around the contraction for each set of words.

1. they have	the've they've theyv'e	**2.** can not	ca'nt canot can't
3. did not	didn't don't di'dnt	**4.** was not	wa'snot wasnot wasn't
5. is not	isnot isn't i'snnt	**6.** were not	weren't we'rent were'nt
7. has not	hisn't hasn't hassn't	**8.** we have	we've we're weve
9. I have	I ha've I'hve I've	**10.** you have	yo'uve you've y'uve
11. will not	willn't will't won't	**12.** would not	wou'ldnt wo'ldt wouldn't

Contractions

Write the two words that make each contraction.

1. aren't	2. didn't	3. wasn't	4. you're
_____	_____	_____	_____
5. isn't	6. couldn't	7. won't	8. I'm
_____	_____	_____	_____

Underline the contraction in each sentence. Write the two words that make the contraction on the line.

1. You're new here, right?   _____

2. Come on, let's take a walk.   _____

3. I'll show you around the town.   _____

4. Oh, there's my friend Joey.   _____

5. You'll like him.   _____

6. We've been friends for a long time.   _____

Plurals

Draw a circle around the word that names each picture.

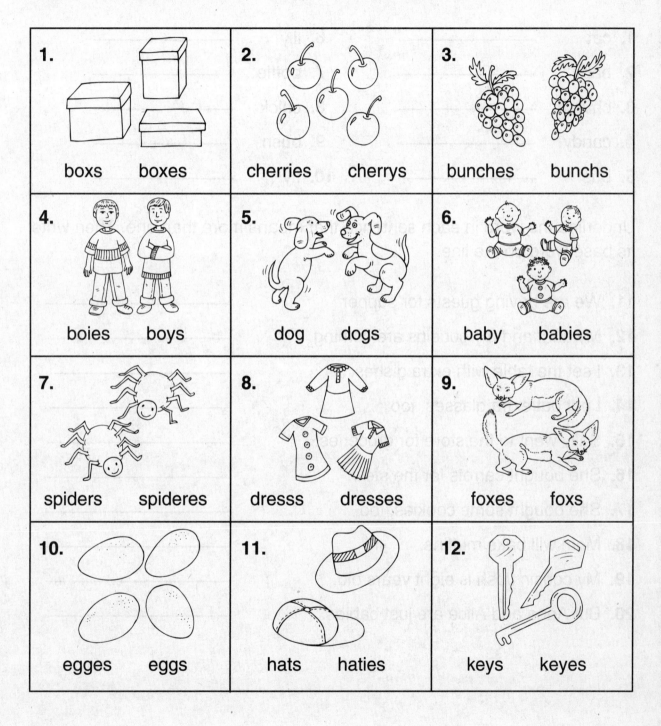

1. boxs   boxes

2. cherries   cherrys

3. bunches   bunchs

4. boies   boys

5. dog   dogs

6. baby   babies

7. spiders   spideres

8. dresss   dresses

9. foxes   foxs

10. egges   eggs

11. hats   haties

12. keys   keyes

Plurals

Write the plural form of the word.

1. cat _____
2. baby _____
3. church _____
4. candy _____
5. bus _____

6. lily _____
7. bottle _____
8. chick _____
9. bush _____
10. fly _____

Underline the word in each sentence that means more than one. Then write its base word on the line.

11. We are having guests for supper. _____

12. My aunt and my cousins are coming. _____

13. I set the table with extra dishes. _____

14. I put out extra glasses, too. _____

15. Sally went to the store for groceries. _____

16. She bought carrots for the stew. _____

17. She bought some cookies, too. _____

18. Mom will bake muffins. _____

19. My cousin Josh is eight years old. _____

20. But Anna and Alice are just babies. _____

Suffixes and Inflectional Endings

Draw a circle around the word that completes the sentence and write it on the line.

1. Now Billy is sitting in a _____ chair.

   comforted   comfortable   comforts

2. Last night Jamie had a _____ night.

   sleeper   sleeps   sleepless

3. Rosa was _____ and could not sit still during the movie.

   rester   resty   restless

4. A cozy chair and soft music make me feel _____.

   sleep   sleepy   sleepless

5. Our dog slept _____ during the thunderstorm.

   sounder   soundness   soundly

6. Yesterday Nancy _____ me on the phone.

   calls   called   calling

7. That new building is the _____ one in town.

   tall   tallest   taller

8. That clown is _____ up and down.

   jumping   jumped   jumps

9. A car is _____ than an airplane.

   slow   slower   slowest

10. Joanna_____the bus.

    miss   missing   missed

Suffixes and Inflectional Endings

Read each sentence. Add a suffix from the box to the word on the right that completes the sentence. Write the new word on the line.

ful	ous	ly

1. Jim thought snow boarding was _____ danger
   until he learned how.

2. He is still _____ though.   care

3. He loves to glide _____ down the hill.   swift

4. He is more _____ than I am.   courage

5. I am happy to sit wrapped _____ in a   snug
   blanket and watch.

Read each word in the word box below. Make new words by adding inflectional endings. Write the new words in the correct column.

walk	kind	fond	soft	call

    er   **est**   **ed**   **ing**

1. _____ _____   4. _____ _____

2. _____ _____   5. _____ _____

3. _____ _____

Prefixes

Read the story. Underline the words with prefixes and write them on the lines. Then draw a circle around the prefix in the words.

Jan was worried because her dog had disappeared again.

"Why does he run away?" she asked. "Is he unhappy here?"

Pat calmed her fears. "Chipper always returns," he said.

"That's true, but I wish he wouldn't disobey me," wailed Jan. "He misbehaves a lot."

"Maybe you need to retrain him," suggested Pat. "Maybe he's uncertain about what you want."

"Maybe you're right," said Jan.

Just then, Chipper reappeared, covered with mud.

"Oh, Chipper!" laughed Jan. "It's back to school for you!"

_____   _____

_____   _____

_____   _____

_____   _____

Prefixes

Read each sentence. Add a prefix from the box to the word on the right to make a word that completes the sentence. Write the new word on the line.

mis	pre	re	dis	un

1. Peggy's Dad writes movie _____ for the   views
   town newspaper.

2. He took us to see a _____ of a new movie.   view

3. I thought the plot was confusing and _____ .   clear

4. I _____ the ending, too.   understood

5. Peggy _____ . She thought the movie   agreed
   was great!

Draw a line from the prefix in the first column to the word in the second column to make a word. Write the word on the line.

6. dis	do	_____	11. de	happy	_____
7. ex	clear	_____	12. mis	respect	_____
8. mis	port	_____	13. dis	paint	_____
9. re	pronounce	_____	14. un	understand	_____
10. un	appear	_____	15. re	frost	_____

Name_____ Date_____

Prefixes

Draw a circle around the word that completes the sentence.
Then write it on the line.

1. It was a cold night, and before we could start, Dad

   had to _____ the car windows.
   detour   fog   defog

2. "You should turn on the _____, too," suggested Mom.
   deport   defroster   demand

3. We headed down the road, but soon we came to a sign. "Oh, no!" said

   Dad. "We have to take a _____."
   defrost   detail   detour

4. "I guess they decided to _____ the work on this part of
   the road," I said.   extend   extra   except

5. Dad was _____ of which way to go, but then we saw more
   signs.
   unopen   sure   uncertain

6. "I don't _____ being on this road before," Mom said.
   retell   unclear   recall

7. "I hope I didn't _____ the signs," said Dad.
   misread   misplace   mission

8. "I thought they were _____, too," I added.
   unopen   unable   unclear

9. Finally we stopped at a gas station and the owner _____
   the right way to go.   expected   explained   expert

10. At last we found the restaurant and made our pizza _____
    quickly!   disappear   disagree   dishonest

Prefixes

Draw a line to the word that answers each riddle. Draw a circle around the prefix in each word.

1. This word means to judge wrongly.

2. You may get into trouble if you do this.

3. If you want to see a video over again, you must do this to it.

4. If you study something and then tell about it, you give this.

5. This word means "to say the wrong thing."

6. If you open the buttons on your coat, you do this.

7. If you faint, you are this.

8. If you take the cover off something, you do this.

9. If you take this, you change the way you are going.

10. If a door is not locked, it is this.

11. If you fight for someone, or keep them safe from danger, you do this.

12. This word means the same as uncertain.

13. This word means to get bigger.

14. If something can't be seen anymore, it has done this.

15. If someone lends you money, you must do this.

misbehave
misjudge
report
detour
rewind
uncover
misspeak
unlocked
unconscious
defend
repay
unbutton
disappeared
unsure
expand

Root Words

Write the base word for each word.

1. pointed _____

2. misread _____

3. disagree _____

4. quickly _____

5. joyous _____

6. poisonous _____

7. reviewed _____

8. discontinue _____

9. replace _____

10. babies _____

11. uncomfortable _____

12. misunderstand _____

13. reread _____

14. softly _____

15. mispronounced _____

16. displease _____

17. disobey _____

18. fatter _____

19. rewind _____

20. remaking _____

Root Words

In the sentences below, underline the words that have a suffix or prefix. Write the words on the lines. Then draw a circle around the root word.

1. We had an eventful day.

2. Our class previewed a new video in science class.

3. We had a discussion and recalled what we saw.

4. Then our teacher rewound the tape and replayed our favorite part.

5. We also reviewed our lines for the play.

6. My character in the play talks directly to the audience.

7. I practiced and quietly reread my lines rapidly to myself.

8. I spoke quickly and nervously at first.

9. Finally, I felt comfortable.

10. I hope I will not sound unsure of myself on the night of the play.

_____ _____ _____

_____ _____ _____

_____ _____ _____

_____ _____ _____

_____ _____

_____

Unit 5 Review

Draw a line from a syllable in the first column to a syllable in the second column to make a word.

act	dle	catch	ner
rid	or	pur	er
car	dle	part	ble
mid	dle	old	ple
pad	ton	crum	er

Now use the words you made to answer the riddles. Write the words on the lines.

1. Someone you work with. _____

2. Mix red and blue to get this color. _____

3. The opposite of younger. _____

4. Something you need in a canoe. _____

5. This is usually made of cardboard. _____

6. The pitcher throws to this person. _____

7. Not at the ends. _____

8. To break into little pieces. _____

9. He acts in a play. _____

10. A word puzzle to work out or guess. _____

Name_____ Date_____

Unit 5 Review

Read the sentences. Underline the contractions and draw a circle around the words that mean more than one. Then write the words in the columns below.

1. "These aren't the thimbles I asked for!" shouted the queen.

2. "You've brought the wrong ones!"

3. "We didn't mean to, Your Majesty," cried the silly servants.

4. "Find the right boxes," said the advisors, "or you're all fired."

5. "We'll do it right this time," said the chief Silly, wringing his hands.

6. "Your wishes are our command," they said.

7. "You'd better!" said the Chief Advisor.

8. "We're in trouble," mumbled the silly helpers.

9. "I'll think of some ideas," said the first silly servant.

10. "She'll have our heads, and he'll do it."

Contractions	Words that Make Contractions	Plurals	Root Words
_____	_____	_____	_____
_____	_____	_____	_____
_____	_____	_____	_____
_____	_____	_____	_____
_____	_____	_____	_____
_____	_____	_____	_____
_____	_____	_____	_____
_____	_____	_____	_____

McGraw-Hill School Division

114 Unit 5 Review

Grade 3 / 30

Unit 5 Review

Read the following sentences. Underline the words that have suffixes or prefixes. Then write the root words on the lines.

1. "Watch me make this rabbit disappear," said the magician.

2. He waved his magic wand over the rabbit three times.

3. He covered the table and the rabbit with a blue silk cloth.

4. Then just as quickly, he uncovered it.

5. Suddenly, the rabbit was gone!

6. The audience applauded loudly.

7. "Now can you make it reappear?" someone asked.

8. The magician blushed.

9. "That part is harder," he said.

10. "I haven't learned that yet," he admitted.

_____   _____   _____

_____   _____   _____

_____   _____   _____

_____   _____   _____

_____   _____   _____

Unit 5 Review

Write each word in syllables.

purple	wonder	actor	sender	misspell
unread	bubble	farmer	simple	hardest

_____   _____

_____   _____

_____   _____

_____   _____

_____   _____

Find the word in the box to finish each sentence. Write the word on the line.

useless	mysterious	I'll	what's	simple
oddest	pondered	predict	lifted	carton

1. There was a strange and _____ cardboard
   _____ on Bill's porch.

2. "_____ in it?" he wondered.

3. While he _____ this question, he stared at the box.

4. "It is the _____ box I've ever seen," he said.

5. Finally, he said, "It is _____ to wonder."

6. "There's a _____ way to find out."

7. So, he _____ the lid.

8. Can you _____ what he found?

9. Well, _____ never tell!

For the next few days the friends practiced hard. Anthony rehearsed his saxophone number. Tim repeated his tumbling act over and over. Tina practiced her magic act privately.

Sue finally stopped following Anthony. It looked as if she had really disappeared.

Finally it was time to set up Pam's garage for the show. Tina came in carrying a long extension cord to use for a special light. She also brought a large box wrapped in silver paper.

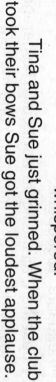

"Here I am!" called Sue, reappearing in the back of the garage.

"How did you do that?" Anthony whispered.

Tina and Sue just grinned. When the club took their bows Sue got the loudest applause.

Fold the right side back on the long center line. Then fold the top half under the bottom half on the short center line. Cut open the tops of the pages.

The next day the Explorers' Club met in Pam's backyard to make posters.

"See the Amazing Tumbling Tim," said one poster.

"Tina, the Marvelous Magician," said another.

"Astounding Animal Acts," said another.

"Those are my two poodles, Choco and Fifi," Pam explained.

The Disappearing Act

"We've got to raise money if we're going to take a trip," said Anthony. It was the Explorers' Club weekly meeting.

"Let's put on a show!" suggested Pam.

The night of the show came. The audience applauded Tim's acrobatic act and clapped in time to Anthony's sax solo.

Tina did her card tricks. She made everyone laugh as she guessed the card they had picked, and found the card in someone's pocket.

Finally she announced, "Now I'll call on my trusty assistant." Sue came out and bowed. Everyone applauded. Anthony groaned, but then he grinned.

Tina assisted Sue to climb into the box on the table. She waved a magic wand and said "Abracadabra! Disappear!"

Just then, all the lights went out! The garage was totally dark. For a minute no one moved.

"Kazoom!" yelled Tina. Suddenly the lights came back on.

"Look!" she cried, showing everyone the empty box. "It's empty!" The audience applauded loudly.

The Disappearing Act McGraw-Hill School Division

The next afternoon, Sue was sitting on her porch with Tina.

"You look unhappy, Sue," said Tina.

"Tina, can I be in the show? Please," begged Sue.

"We'll think of something," Tina promised. She thought for a minute then said, "I think I have an idea! What was it Anthony said?"

"Great idea," said Tim. "I've got some new stunts I can do."

"I'll display my new card tricks," added Tina.

"What can I do?" asked Sue. "I want to be in the show."

"You're too little," said Anthony. "You're not even in the club."

"That's not fair!" said Sue.

"Oh, don't be mean, Anthony," said Tina. "We can figure out something for Sue."

"I wish she'd disappear," said Anthony.

Name_____ Date_____

Synonyms

Find two words in the box that go with each picture. Write them on the lines.

cheering	cleaning	cutting	dash	draw	explain
fire	flames	frightened	iron	napping	paring
peeling	press	rooting	rush	scared	scrubbing
sketch	slicing	sobbing	snoozing	teach	tearful

1.

_____

_____

2.

_____

_____

3.

_____

_____

4.

_____

_____

5.

_____

_____

6.

_____

_____

7.

_____

_____

8.

_____

_____

9.

_____

_____

10.

_____

_____

11.

_____

_____

12.

_____

_____

Name_____ Date_____

Synonyms

Draw a line from each word in the first column to its synonym in the second column.

1. develop	mug	11. section	symbol
2. back	journey	12. scores	cover
3. think	charge	13. work	toil
4. brags	dirt	14. wrap	grades
5. cup	ripen	15. harvest	sum
6. travel	rear	16. wise	questions
7. checks	protect	17. sign	part
8. soil	boasts	18. set	place
9. fee	believe	19. asks	clever
10. guard	looks	20. total	pick

Use the words from above to finish the sentences in the story.

When I bring home my report card with good _____,
my mom smiles. She often _____ about me to Grandma.
Mom doesn't know it, but Grandma sometimes _____
my math papers. She makes sure that when I add, I get the right

_____.

She and I love to _____ in the garden together. I
really like digging up the _____ and planting seeds.
Grandma works in one _____ of the garden and I work
in another. Sometimes we take a break, and I run in to get her a

_____ of water. We enjoy watching the vegetables grow

and _____. Both of us can't wait until we can

_____ them and cook them.

McGraw-Hill School Division

120 Synonyms

Grade 3 **30**

Synonyms

Find a synonym in the box for each underlined word. Write it on the line.

back	build	completed	create	drawing	happy
likes	many	paste	ill	space	surfaces

1. Brenda loves to <u>make</u> sand pictures. _____

2. First, she makes a <u>sketch</u> of what she wants each picture to look like.

   _____

3. Then she uses <u>glue</u> where she wants the sand to stick. _____

4. Next, she pours different colors of sand on the <u>areas</u> with the

   glue. _____

5. When her picture is <u>finished</u>, she tacks it on the bulletin board.

   _____

6. David likes to <u>construct</u> houses with logs and blocks. _____

7. Sometimes he makes one with <u>multiple</u> rooms. _____

8. Sometimes he adds a <u>rear</u> door. _____

9. One time he made <u>room</u> for a fireplace but forgot to add a chimney.

   _____

10. No matter! Everyone <u>enjoys</u> looking at the houses he builds.

    _____

11. When someone in class is home <u>sick</u>, we all make "get-well

    cards." _____

12. We write <u>cheerful</u> notes to make the person feel better. _____

Synonyms

Read each word. Find its synonym in the word box to complete the puzzle.

cash	charge	fast	festival	part
occurs	pare	repair	ripen	surprise
surround	tie	top	traded	trip

Across

1. fair

4. fix

5. lid

6. piece

7. develop

9. border

11. knot

12. money

13. fee

Down

1. quick

2. astonish

3. exchanged

8. peel

10. happens

11. journey

McGraw-Hill School Division

Antonyms

Draw a line from each word in the first column to its antonym in the second column.

1. buy	sorrow	11. bottom	begin
2. tight	interested	12. noise	absent
3. new	wide	13. stop	wrong
4. quickly	apart	14. refuse	fix
5. joy	sell	15. present	enemy
6. bored	loose	16. break	accept
7. narrow	serious	17. speak	fantasy
8. together	dull	18. correct	top
9. funny	old	19. real	listen
10. sharp	slowly	20. friend	quiet

Cross out each underlined word below and replace it with an antonym from above.

It's fun to write real _____ stories about dragons. My

enemy _____ and I sometimes work apart

_____ to make the story as serious

_____ as we can. It takes us awhile to do a good job.

We work quickly _____. We want the people who speak

_____ to our story, to be bored _____.

It takes just a moment after we stop _____ to know if

they are laughing. It gives us sorrow _____ to know that

they like our story. Someday I hope that I will be able to buy

_____ my work.

Antonyms

Draw a circle around the antonym that will make sense in the sentence.
Then write the new sentence on the line.

1. It is (boring, exciting) to go to an amusement park.

_____

2. When the roller coaster (climbs, descends) up to the sky, I usually
am calm.

_____

3. But when it speeds down the track I usually (whisper, yell) for help.

_____

4. My (buddies, foes) always tease me.

_____

5. But I know they too are (scared, unafraid) when they are on the ride.

_____

6. They don't (hide, display) their emotions like I do.

_____

7. We all like to walk through the (serious, amusing) house of mirrors.

_____

8. Sarah is quite thin, but in front of the mirror, she is as (tiny,
enormous) as a giant.

_____

9. At a booth we (caught, tossed) rings around bottles.

_____

10. Jose won a (dull, bright) hot pink and green yo-yo.

_____

McGraw-Hill School Division

Antonyms

Find the antonymn in the box for each word. Write it on the line.

absent	break	dry	fact	false
light	melt	tardy	tiny	weak

1. gigantic _____
2. freeze _____
3. heavy _____
4. true _____
5. mighty _____

6. present _____
7. mend _____
8. moist _____
9. early _____
10. fiction _____

Cross out the word in the sentence that makes it false. Find an antonym above that will make the sentence correct and write it on the line.

1. Ice will melt at 32 degrees. _____

2. The tardy bird catches the worm. _____

3. It's easy to use a dry sponge. _____

4. A feather is quite heavy. _____

5. A story about a unicorn must be fact. _____

6. If you mend a toy in a store, you have to buy it. _____

7. Only if you are absent, will you be able to vote. _____

8. I've never seen a gigantic elephant. _____

9. It is true that all birds fly. _____

10. If you are early you will not find a seat up front. _____

Antonyms

Read each word. Find its antonym in the word box to complete the puzzle. Then read the shaded boxes to find out where many teenagers like to go.

back	begin	cellar	cooked	arrive
dead	dry	keep	long	near
open	silent	straight	take	thin

1. give

2. end

3. noisy

4. crooked

5. leave

6. shut

7. attic

8. release

9. raw

10. short

11. far

12. front

13. alive

14. moist

15. broad

Name_____ Date_____

Homonyms

Draw a line from each word in the first column to its homonym in the second column.

1. blew	made	**6.** week	beat
2. or	won	**7.** rode	so
3. maid	dye	**8.** beet	do
4. die	blue	**9.** due	weak
5. one	oar	**10.** sew	road

Draw a circle around the homonym that makes sense in the sentence. Then write the new sentence on the line.

11. It is (night/knight) time.

_____

12. All you can (see/sea) is the raccoon's (tale/tail).

_____

13. It looks like the raccoon (ate/ eight) some fruit from a tree.

_____

14. Maybe that (bear/bare) won't spot him up in the tree.

_____

15. (eye/I) think the raccoon will (weight/ wait) until the big (won/one) leaves.

_____

16. I hope it will not (be/bee) more than an (our/hour).

_____

Homonyms

Find the homonym in the box for each underlined word. Then write the new sentence on the line.

aunt	buy	know	one	ring	red
road	stare	steak	tails	to	write

1. Last week my <u>ant</u> took me to a county fair.

_____

2. The fare was <u>won</u> dollar for me and two for her.

_____

3. The first event we went <u>too</u> watch was a pig race.

_____

4. I just love the pigs' curly <u>tales</u>.

_____

5. I could not help but <u>stair</u> at the clown who was walking on his

hands. _____

_____

6. Then I went to <u>by</u> some cotton candy.

_____

7. She said, "Don't you <u>no</u> how bad that is for your teeth?"

_____

8. I also bought a pretty <u>wring</u> for my finger.

_____

Homonyms

Draw a line from each word in the first column to its homonym in the second column.

1. through	cent	6. bow	sun
2. would	male	7. sale	sail
3. scent	sore	8. son	bough
4. mail	wood	9. pale	wail
5. soar	threw	10. whale	pail

Use the words from above to finish the sentences.

11. I am proud of my _____.

12. No matter what the weather, he delivers the _____ every day.

13. Some days his feet get very _____.

14. My face turned _____ when I looked at the blisters on his feet.

15. I _____ up my hands and said you have to go to the doctor.

16. He said he _____ not do that.

17. Instead he soaked his feet in a _____ of water.

18. He promised to buy some new hiking boots that are on _____.

19. He wants them so he can walk _____ the mud and snow.

20. I felt better and went to get some _____ for the fire.

Homonyms

Read each word. Find its homonym in the word box to complete the puzzle.

aunt	bear	fair	flea	hare	lead	maid	meat
road	sail	sew	stare	sun	tale	through	

Across

1. tail

4. rode

5. meet

6. fare

7. hair

10. sale

11. stair

Down

1. threw

2. led

3. bare

6. flee

8. ant

9. made

10. so

11. son

Homographs

Read the sentence. Then write on the line the letter of the picture that goes with the underlined word.

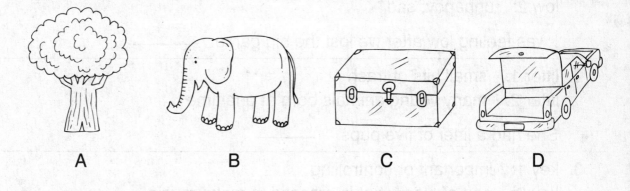

A   B   C   D

1. Dad opened the <u>trunk</u> to see if the bookshelf would fit. _____

2. Wouldn't it be grand to have a <u>trunk</u> that you can move back and forth? _____

3. You can tell its age by the size of its <u>trunk</u>. _____

4. That <u>trunk</u> will fit in the back seat of the car. _____

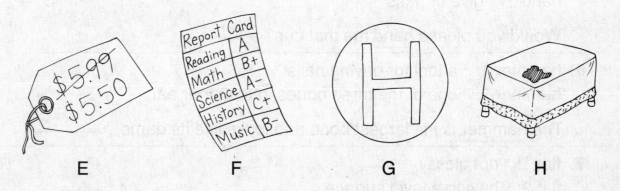

E   F   G   H

5. What <u>mark</u> did you get in Reading? _____

6. That is the <u>mark</u> for a hospital; one is close by. _____

7. If you <u>mark</u> it down, I will save about fifty cents. _____

8. Let's hope that that <u>mark</u> will come out in the wash. _____

Homographs

Write the number 1 or 2 to show which definition goes with the sentence.

1. low 1:   not high or tall
   low 2:   unhappy; sad

   I was feeling <u>low</u> after we lost the big game.   ———

2. litter 1:   small bits of trash
   litter 2:   many young animals born at one time

   She had a <u>litter</u> of five pups.   ———

3. key 1:   important or controlling
   key 2:   part of piano that is pressed to make music

   She was the <u>key</u> player in that group.   ———

4. jam 1:   press or squeeze into a tight place
   jam 2:   to push with force

   Dad <u>jammed</u> on the brakes when he saw that truck.   ———

5. hand 1:   one of the pointers on a clock
   hand 2:   give or pass

   Would you please <u>hand</u> me that cup?   ———

6. hammer 1:   a tool for driving nails
   hammer 2:   one of the three bones in the inner ear

   The <u>hammer</u> is the largest bone and looks like its name.   ———

7. flat 1:   not glossy
   flat 2:   having a level surface

   Mom used a <u>flat</u> blue paint in my room.   ———

8. tie 1:   to fasten by knotting a string or cord; make a bow
   tie 2:   an even score

   The baby is trying to <u>tie</u> her shoelaces.   ———

Homographs

Read each sentence and look at the underlined word. Write the number of the definition of the word.

run 1:	to move quickly	run 7:	to spread or get mixed
run 2:	to make a journey	run 8:	to keep working
run 3:	to flow or cause to flow	run 9:	to climb or grow in long shoots
run 4:	to take part in a race or contest	run 10:	to be in charge or put in operation
run 5:	to become torn; unravel		
run 6:	to publish or print		

1. When we wash the new shirt, I hope the colors will not <u>run</u>. ——

2. We want to <u>run</u> an ad in the newspaper about our lost puppy. ——

3. No matter what we did, we could not make the clock <u>run</u>. ——

4. Mom got a <u>run</u> in her stocking. ——

5. I <u>ran</u> to the store for my aunt. ——

6. That vine <u>ran</u> up the long pole. ——

7. He has been hired as manager to <u>run</u> the new shop. ——

8. Dad had to <u>run</u> up to Boston for a meeting. ——

turn 1:	to cause to move	turn 4:	to change to something different
turn 2:	to change direction	turn 5:	a regular time or chance
turn 3:	to go from one thing to another		

1. Please <u>turn</u> left at the corner. ——

2. It is my <u>turn</u> to spin the dial. ——

3. Will you please <u>turn</u> to page 54? ——

4. If you <u>turn</u> the key, the door will open. ——

5. The water <u>turned</u> to ice so quickly. ——

McGraw-Hill School Division

Homographs

Write a sentence using each word as it is defined.

1. tear: to pull apart or rip

_____

2. tear: a drop of salty liquid that falls from the eyes

_____

3. tape: a narrow strip with a sticky side

_____

4. tape: to record

_____

5. strike: to hit

_____

6. strike: a pitch that the batter misses

_____

7. stand: a booth where things are sold

_____

8. stand: to be on your feet; to rise to your feet.

_____

9. spin: to make fibers into thread or yarn

_____

10. spin: to turn or whirl about

_____

Unit 6 Review

Read each pair of words. Write **S** if they are synonyms. Write **A** if they are antonyms, and write **H** if they are homonyms

1. fast/quick _____

2. sore/soar _____

3. flour/flower _____

4. silent/noisy _____

5. silly/comical _____

6. brake/stop _____

7. break/brake _____

8. take/give _____

9. reality/fantasy _____

10. exchange/trade _____

11. glisten/sparkle _____

12. freeze/melt _____

13. liquid/solid _____

14. add/subtract _____

15. heel/heal _____

16. damp/moist _____

17. broad/wide _____

18. narrow/thick _____

19. charming/cute _____

20. pair/pare _____

Read the sentence. Then write on the line the letter of the picture that goes with the underlined word.

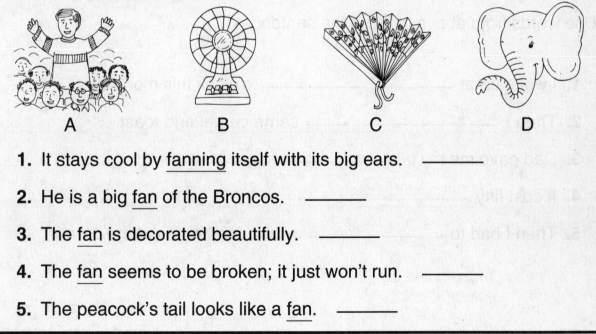

A   B   C   D

1. It stays cool by <u>fanning</u> itself with its big ears. _____

2. He is a big <u>fan</u> of the Broncos. _____

3. The <u>fan</u> is decorated beautifully. _____

4. The <u>fan</u> seems to be broken; it just won't run. _____

5. The peacock's tail looks like a <u>fan</u>. _____

Unit 6 Review

Write an antonym for each word.

1. minus _____
2. death _____
3. long _____
4. near _____
5. speak _____

6. fix _____
7. question _____
8. frown _____
9. wee _____
10. work _____

Write a homonym for each word.

11. fare _____
12. two _____
13. sense _____
14. weight _____
15. knight _____

16. knot _____
17. see _____
18. aunt _____
19. one _____
20. eight _____

Use words from above to finish the sentences.

1. I woke up at _____ o'clock this morning.

2. Then I _____ some cereal and toast.

3. Dad gave me my bus _____.

4. It cost fifty _____.

5. Then I had to _____ for the bus at the corner.

Unit 6 Review

Find a synonym in the word box for each underlined word. Write it on the line.

also	buy	carried	container	dish
finished	lunchroom	many	pal	remained

1. I went to the <u>cafeteria</u>, grabbed a tray, and got at the end of

   the line. _____

2. There were <u>plenty</u> of dishes to choose from. _____

3. I picked up a <u>plate</u> of macaroni. _____

4. I took a red juicy apple, <u>too</u>. _____

5. I <u>took</u> my tray to the table. _____

6. Then I realized I forgot to <u>purchase</u> something to drink. _____

7. I returned and bought a <u>carton</u> of milk. _____

8. When I was <u>through</u> eating, I tossed my litter in the trash

   can. _____

9. Then my <u>friend</u> and I ran out to the playground. _____

10. We <u>stayed</u> there until the bell rang. _____

Write a sentence using each word as it is defined.

11. exercise: active movement of the body

_____

12. exercise: a group of problems or activities

_____

Unit 6 Review

Complete the puzzle.

Across

1. synonym for **comical**

5. antonym for **short**

6. synonym for **sob**

7. synonym for **edge**

9. antonym for **on**

10. homonym for **eight**

11. homonym for **two**

12. homonym for **pare**

13. synonym for **all right**, slang

15. homonym for **real**

16. synonym for **pile**

18. homonym for **lead**

19. synonym for **ill**

20. homonym for **sea**

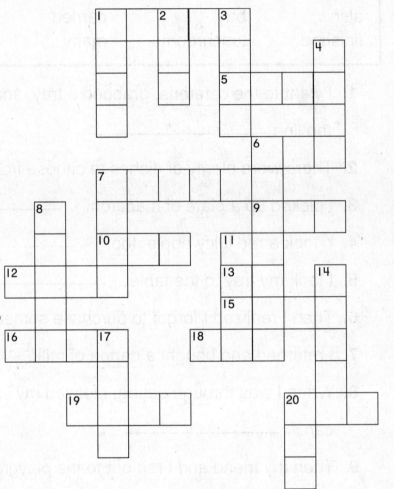

Down

1. synonym for **fee**

2. homonym for **knot**

3. synonym for **shout**

4. antonym for **pretty**

6. antonym for **straight**

7. homonym for **bare**

8. synonym for **exchange**

11. synonym for **ripped**

14. antonym for **dead**

17. homonym for **pane**

20. homonym for **so**

McGraw-Hill School Division

For Natasha's sake, you point to the bag of *flour* and say flour; then you point to the *flower* and say flower.

Then Natasha says, "I know, I know." But when you ask her to put in two cups of flour and she picks up the flower, you have to say, "No, no! I know for sure you don't understand."

Somehow, Natasha's feelings aren't hurt. The cake turns out well, and everyone has a *piece* for dessert.

Natasha's Visit McGraw-Hill School Division

So you don't forget, you run into the kitchen and put the note on the fridge. Then you decide to bake a cake. You get out the milk, eggs, butter, and some flour. Your Mom walks in with a huge flower from the garden and puts it in a vase.

You might say to her, "I'm so glad to *meet* you." Then you could take her out for a hamburger. You could explain, "It's *meat* on a *roll.*" She scratches her head. How can *meet* and *meat* be so different?

Later, you decide to tell her a story, a *tale* about when you were a baby. You take out your album. Just then your dog comes running past and hits you with its *tail.* You *roll* a ball for him to chase so he will get out of your way.

Mom sits down to read the book *War and Peace*. I say, "Since we ate all of the cake, I'll go *by* the bakery and *buy* another one tomorrow."

Dad says, "Yes, that's a good idea."

Mom says, "No, that's a bad idea. I need to lose some weight."

Natasha and I look at each other and *roll* our eyes.

Fold the right side back on the long center line. Then fold the top half under the bottom half on the short center line. Cut open the tops of the pages.

Natasha's Visit

Pretend you had a visitor who came from another country. We'll call her Natasha. Natasha does not speak a word of English. How would you help her get to know her way around?

You bring out a *tape* of your favorite songs to play on the stereo for Natasha. You both enjoy the music. You even dance a little. Then your mom asks you to please remember to *tape* a note from the dentist on the refrigerator door.